The Ray Society
INSTITUTED 1844

This volume is No. 157 of the series

LONDON

1986

To Kris

Figurehead of H.M.S. Challenger, *now over the main entrance to the Institute of Oceanographic Sciences at Wormley in Surrey. The figurehead was presented to I.O.S. by the Hydrographer, Rear Admiral G.P.D. Hall, in June, 1973. For some years previously the figurehead had stood at the official residence of the Commander-in-Chief, Fleet, at Northwood, and prior to that in the figurehead collection at Chatham.*

BRITISH OCEANOGRAPHIC VESSELS
1800 - 1950

A. L. RICE, D.Sc.

Institute of Oceanographic Sciences,
Wormley, Godalming, Surrey

ISBN 0 903874 19 9

Sold by The Ray Society,
c/o British Museum (Natural History), Cromwell Road, London SW7 5BD

Typeset in 10 point Bembo and printed by
Minerva Press, Brentwood, Essex CM13 1TF

CONTENTS

Frontispiece.
H.M.S. Lightning, *under the command of Capt. B.J. Sulivan, leading British screwships through the Anga Channel in the Aland Islands towards Bomarsund on July 22, 1854, during the Baltic campaign. Artist O.W. Brierly. Courtesy National Maritime Museum.*

By the time the Lightning *made her short contribution to oceanography in 1868 the tiny paddle steamer was already 45 years old and was quite unsuited for the role she had to play. Nevertheless, discoveries made during her eight week voyage to the north and west of the British Isles totally changed the accepted concepts of deep-sea biology and physics, arguably making this cruise even more important, day for day, than that of the* Challenger.

FOREWORD

The amount of literature available on the early development of the marine sciences has greatly increased during the twenty years which have passed since the first International Congress on the History of Oceanography was held at Monaco in 1966. Nevertheless, notwithstanding the interest generated by the centenary of the voyage of H.M.S. *Challenger,* only a few years after that, more attention has been directed to looking at the work of individuals, and to ideas and methods, than to oceanographic expeditions and the ships in which they were made. This is especially true for Britain. Whereas American vessels have their own official history, *Oceanographic Ships—Fore and Aft,* first published in 1971, as well as books such as Susan Schlee's story of the *Atlantis* and Woods Hole, *On Almost Any Wind,* no comprehensive work on British ships and expeditions has appeared up to now.

Practical considerations have made it necessary for Tony Rice to limit the coverage he has given. Scientific research at sea did not of course begin in 1800 but most scientists interested in making such observations in the 17th and 18th centuries had to do so at second hand. Robert Boyle was fortunate in being a director of the East India Company. Stephen Hales had contacts with slave ships through his interest in shipboard ventilation and observations with his 'bucket' were made by the ship *Earl of Hallifax.* Captain Charles Douglas made similar observations for Professor Alexander Wilson of Glasgow in 1769 in H.M.S. *Emerald.* Very often, however, we do not know even the name of the ships in which the few observations or tests of apparatus were made, which carried the Fellows of the Royal Society to try out their machine for sounding without a line, and other experiments, in the Solent and the Medway in 1662 and early 1663, or which made the unsuccessful attempt with Hales's sounding machine near Bermuda in the 1730s. Lacking this basic information on so many occasions, an attempt to list ships involved in observations of an oceanographic nature before 1800 would be necessarily less complete and, because of the very different state of the science at that time, more of an antiquarian exercise than for the later period where details are also important to modern researchers who may wish to make use of the data.

The first voyages to be undertaken primarily for scientific research at sea, and in a ship built specially for the purpose, were those of Edmond Halley in the *Paramore* pink. On the first two, in 1698-1700, he measured magnetic variation in the North and South Atlantic Oceans and on the third, in 1701, the tidal streams of the English Channel. It was the difficulties experienced by Halley with his officers that led the Admiralty, many years later, to appoint Cook, and not a civilian scientist or geographer, to search for the southern continent. Halley was keenly interested in the application of his scientific results to practical problems and hoped that both his magnetic and tidal charts would be useful navigational aids, as well as promoting more fundamental understanding; but, though he noted the condition of sea and weather during his voyages, he seems to have attempted no specifically oceanographic, or sub-surface, observations, perhaps because of the difficulties other workers such as Hooke had encountered in developing reliable apparatus.

The first major British expedition to carry out a variety of oceanographic work was in 1773 when Captain C.J. Phipps, in command of H.M. Ships *Racehorse* and *Carcass,* made an attempt to sail to the North Pole, testing the claim by some geographers that the Arctic Ocean was free of ice. Phipps made two deep-sea soundings, one successful, and experimented with different methods of measuring deep-sea temperatures. The interest of the scientific work made up for the expedition's failure to penetrate the Arctic pack-ice. The young Horatio Nelson had a narrow escape from a polar bear.

The voyages of Captain Cook also saw the collection of some oceanographic data, though the effort here was less concerted, and formed only a minor part of the scientific achievements of the three expeditions. Some sea-surface measurements of temperature and specific gravity were taken, and some tidal observations, but the most interesting observations, both to contemporary geographers and later researchers, were the few recorded measurements of sub-surface temperature, carried out as the result of the Board of Longitude's instructions to their astronomers on the second voyage, William Wales and William Bayly, since they showed the temperature inversion in the surface layers of the Southern Ocean.

By the early 1800s scientific research was well established as an integral feature of maritime exploration, now principally directed to the Pacific and polar regions, and was to become an increasingly important part of such proceedings. However, because of the sheer difficulty of making sub-surface observations, oceanographic work remained rather marginal and was usually only undertaken if the explorer or surveyor had a personal interest in the subject. Things began to change in the middle years of the century when submarine cable laying led to the creation of technology for working in deep water and scientific exploration of the deep sea at last became a practical possibility. Britain played a considerable part in these developments, though they were by no means confined to these shores, and continued to make interesting contributions to the new science of oceanography, though opportunities were limited and money generally tight. Partly for this reason not all British work was done in British ships! In 1910 Sir John Murray borrowed the fishery research vessel *Michael Sars* and her scientific staff from the Norwegian Government, paying the expenses himself, for a four month cruise in the North Atlantic. It was not until after World War II that a period of more rapid growth and expansion began. Rightly, Tony Rice brings his work to an end at the beginning of this phase since the volume of work carried out in the last forty years is so great that in a single volume it would crowd out the earlier material. Also, the emphasis has been different, with multi-ship and internationally organized expeditions replacing the older pattern of work.

In dealing with the period between 1800 and 1950, *British Oceanographic Vessels* thus fills the need for a work of reference which will be valuable not only to those interested in the history of oceanography but also to anyone seeking information on scientific exploration at sea in the 19th and early 20th centuries.

M.B. Deacon
Southampton
July 1986

PREFACE

Although this book has been written mainly in my own, or rather my family's, time, it would have been quite beyond my means if I had not had access to the facilities of the Institute of Oceanographic Sciences. I must therefore first express my gratitude to my employers, the Natural Environment Research Council, and more specifically to Martin Angel, the Head of Biology at I.O.S., for allowing me to take advantage so freely of my position on the staff of the Institute.

The most important consequence of this generosity has been access to the help of my Department's Secretary, Pam Talbot, who has seen the task through from beginning to end and has turned my almost illegible, and repeatedly altered, scrawl into a pristine typescript. Despite her unfailing interest and tenacity it is doubtful whether she, or I, would have stayed the course without the unconscious help of her word processor which arrived, like the U.S. Cavalry, in the nick of time!

Second, all of the charts have been prepared by the Biology Department's artist, Christine Darter, who has often improved upon the originals.

Third, the I.O.S. photographers, Arnold Madgwick and Mike Conquer, have worked wonders to produce excellent prints from some very unpromising originals.

My colleague, Michael Thurston, read almost the whole manuscript, unravelling my tortuous English and giving me the benefit of his knowledge of Antarctic literature.

Finally, the librarians, initially under Dick Privett and latterly under Pauline Simpson, have tenaciously chased dozens of obscure references, often from my incomplete or erroneous citations.

Outside the Institute I have received information or help from a wide range of organisation and individuals. The sources of the illustrations are acknowledged in the legends, but since most of them came from museums or other public collections my true benefactors remain anonymous; to all of them I extend my grateful thanks. Similarly, I am grateful to the many friends and colleagues, both in the U.K. and overseas, and including the staffs of the British Museum (Natural History), the Hydrographic Department of the Admiralty, the Marine Biological Association, the Maritime Trust, the National Maritime Museum and the Scott Polar Research Institute, who have freely given me the benefit of their knowledge and experience, often preventing me from making the most glaring of errors.

Most of these helpers must remain anonymous since any attempted listing would be long and incomplete, but a small number demand specific mention. David Henderson of the City of Dundee Museums provided me with information on several Dundee whalers which I would never otherwise have found; Tim Collins of the University College, Galway and John de Courcy Ireland gave me much needed help with the Irish vessels; Rear Admiral R.O. Morris told me of of existence of several important photographs of survey vessels in the Imperial War Museum of which I was totally ignorant; Ann Shirley and David Lyon of the National Maritime Museum read major portions of the typescript and made important and valuable comments and provided me with copious information which was quite unknown to me; above all, I am deeply grateful to Margaret Deacon for her encouragement, for writing the foreword, for commenting on almost the entire typescript, and for presenting me with her own notes on several vessels, and particularly the *Medusa*, which I have used virtually verbatim. Despite all of this help, errors undoubtedly remain and are, of course, entirely my responsibility.

Finally, my gratitude is due to my wife, Kris, who endured my preoccupation with the book for night after night over many months; I hope the result at least partly makes up for her sacrifice.

Tony Rice
Farnham, May, 1986

INTRODUCTION

This volume evolved from a simple index, begun in the late 1970s, intended to save myself looking up the same information repeatedly. Having an interest in the history of oceanography, I had frequently searched for information about this or that vessel during the previous decade for myself, for colleagues or for publishers. Where the enquiry concerned one of the more famous expeditions, such as those of the *Erebus* and *Terror, Challenger* or *Discovery,* this was not too difficult, since so much has been written about these ships both contemporaneously and subsequently. For many of the less well-known vessels, however, it was often necessary to refer to some fairly obscure, and sometimes quite rare, original source. Even obtaining accurate references to such sources frequently proved quite difficult.

There were, of course, a number of very valuable starting points, such as the accounts of the history of oceanography in Wyville Thomson's (1872) *Depths of the Sea,* Murray's (1895) summary volume of the *Challenger Reports,* Murray and Hjort's (1912) *Depths of the Ocean,* and the much more recent excellent general accounts by Margaret Deacon (1971) and Susan Schlee (1975). But none of these were exhaustive, or even attempted to be, and where they mentioned a vessel in which I was interested they often failed to provide the particular information, or the lead to it, that I needed.

Some published lists are exhaustive, or very nearly so, in the areas that they set out to cover. For instance, Tizard's (1900) list of British naval surveying vessels up to that time is amazingly complete; but the information provided for each vessel is extremely restricted, at most including only the captain's name, the broad geographical area in which she worked and some very general indication of the type of work undertaken such as "surveying" or "deep-sea sounding". Moreover, where I have been able to check, the list contains many errors of detail.

Similarly, Roberts' (1958) list of Antarctic expeditions and the Cooke and Holland (1978) similar treatment for the Canadian Arctic are remarkably comprehensive, and considering the number of vessels and expeditions included they both contain a wealth of valuable information for each entry. Nevertheless, in the context of the development of oceanography in general, the coverage in both cases is very limited.

The lists of de Buen (1934) and Bencker (1944) are much broader in scope, but again lack many of the details or references that I have sought, and also repeat the errors of the earlier sources, such as Tizard's list, that they made use of.

In short, there seemed to be no single source to which I could refer which would provide the details I wanted directly, or a reference to another publication where the information could be found. Accordingly, in self defence I began to compile a list of my own; it is from this list that the one presented here has developed.

As an amateur historian of oceanography, the amount of time I have been able to devote to compiling the catalogue has been relatively restricted and very variable from year to year. Initially, I devoted little direct effort to it, but simply noted down odd pieces of information as I came across them in the course of other work. At this stage my notes were very brief indeed, containing no more than the ship's name, the date of its oceanographic cruise or cruises, the scientific leader and commander, and a general indication of where the vessel went and the main categories of work carried out. Gradually, however, it occurred to me that if I found the list useful, other people might also. But to justify its publication for this purpose it clearly had to be extensively refined, if only to avoid some of the shortcomings of the other available published sources.

SCOPE OF THE LIST–CRITERIA FOR INCLUSION

First, within the limits set upon it, the list had to be as exhaustive as I could make it in terms of the vessels dealt with. Setting these limits has proved to be an almost intractable problem, but a number of loose or rather arbitrary criteria have been adopted in an attempt to solve it. My list initially included information on ships belonging to many nations, but it soon became obvious that I would be unable to produce a complete world list of oceanographic vessels in a reasonable time. Consequently, the coverage has been restricted to British vessels, partly because accessibility of the literature and language problems would have made any broader task much more difficult, but also because Britain definitely dominated the early development of oceanography, particularly during much of the nineteenth century.

Next, cut-off dates had to be established. A starting date of 1800 was chosen rather arbitrarily since, prior to the *Challenger* Expedition of 1872 to 1876, or the immediately preceding cruises of the *Lightning* and *Porcupine,* no single event or cruise seems to have been pre-eminently significant. The year finally chosen was certainly no more important in the development of British oceanography than several others that could have been selected in the late eighteenth or early nineteenth centuries. Admittedly, 1800 was the year in which Napoleon despatched the post-revolutionary circumnavigation in the *Géographe* and the *Naturaliste* under Nicolas Baudin, during which the naturalist François Péron made regular observations of the surface temperature and four attempts to measure the sub-surface temperature at different depths. Péron's results were widely quoted on the Continent and had an important influence on views on oceanic circulation (see Deacon, 1985), but apparently had little impact in Britain. In 1801, long before Péron's results were available, Matthew Flinders sailed from England in the *Investigator* for his exploration of Australia, a voyage of enormous geographical significance. At the beginning of the voyage Flinders made regular surface temperature measurements and some sub-surface ones, but after only a few weeks all of his thermometers were broken and these observations came to an end. Apart from William Scoresby's observations from the *Resolution* and the *Esk* there was no further significant British contribution to marine science until after the end of the Napoleonic wars some fifteen years later.

The cut-off date at the recent end was chosen slightly less arbitrarily. Wüst's (1964) analysis of the history of oceanography since the 1872 *Challenger* Expedition suggests that his second phase, that of national systematic and dynamic ocean surveys, came to an end at the outbreak of the Second World War. He further suggests that the next phase, based mainly on new methods in geology and geophysics, biology and physics, ensued from 1947. Between these phases there was a rather marked change in the nature of oceanographic cruises. Although there were important exceptions, oceanographic expeditions before the war tended to be rather protracted, covering large areas of ocean and working widely spaced stations. After the war there was an increasing tendency towards shorter individual cruises with much more specific objectives both in terms of scientific discipline and geographical area. However, in the immediate post-war period four major cruises in the old style took place; the Swedish *Albatross* (1947-48), the Danish *Atlantide* (1945-46) and *Galathea* (1950-52), and the more or less simultaneous world cruise of H.M.S. *Challenger.* I therefore chose 1950, not only because it is the mid-point of the twentieth century, but also because by doing so I included probably the last serious British oceanographic circumnavigation.

Having determined the era to be dealt with, the types of vessel to be included also had to be decided. Prior to the cruise of H.M.S. *Lightning* in 1868 no British vessels were despatched for purely oceanographic purposes. Indeed, at that time marine science was hardly recognised as a distinct discipline and it was not until the 1880s that the term oceanography was coined to describe it (see Deacon, 1971). Consequently, none of the earlier ships can be considered as "oceanographic vessels" in the strict sense. On the other hand, even after the *Challenger* Expedition set the standard for subsequent oceanographic voyages, many important discoveries were made from ships which were not at sea primarily for scientific purposes. A consideration only of vessels with the sole purpose of the acquisition of oceanographic data would therefore be quite unrealistic. Accordingly, I have tried to include all vessels from which significant oceanographic observations were made as long as this work was conducted in the open ocean, that is beyond the Continental Shelf. I have not, therefore, included any of the vessels hired, borrowed or owned by members of the British Association Dredging Committee which were used for extensive dredging cruises around the British Isles during the middle decades of the nineteenth century. Nor, generally, have I included fishery research vessels or the ships operated by the marine laboratories unless, like for instance the *Goldseeker* and the two *Helgas,* they made important, if only occasional, forays into deep water. This criterion has not been applied with total consistency, and entries will be found for several vessels, such as the *Huxley, Garland* and *Granuaile,* for which I can find no evidence of deep sea work, but which I would expect, perhaps irrationally, to be found in such a list since they were closely associated with vessels or projects which did include a significant deep-sea element.

Similarly, despite my declared intention to be as exhaustive as possible, I have not attempted to include all vessels from which any deep sea observation was made, however restricted. I have consequently not included many of the vessels operated by cable companies to survey submarine cable routes, or naval vessels which also obtained deep sea soundings, unless I felt, as in the quite different cases of the *Dacia* or the *Britannia* for example, that they made a more significant contribution to the development of oceanography. I have tried to adopt a similar attitude towards vessels from which occasional sea water samples or temperature and salinity measurements were made. I have therefore included vessels such as the *Thalia,* whose oceanographic contribution was small but significant at the time, but have excluded the ships listed by Matthews (1926) as having made surface observations in the Indian Ocean at the same time as the Percy Sladen Trust Expedition in the *Sealark* in 1905. In the end such decisions are personal and rather arbitrary, and I apologise if my choice does not coincide with that of the reader.

INFORMATION PROVIDED

For those vessels which conformed to these various criteria and are included, the amount of information provided is very variable, again to a large extent reflecting my own preferences or prejudices. However, in each case I have tried, not always successfully, to provide certain basic information about the ship herself, the scientists and mariners associated with her, and what she was used for during her oceanographic involvement and, where possible, during the rest of her career.

Type of vessel

As far as the physical characteristics of each ship are concerned, I have tried to provide a very general description such as "wooden paddle frigate", "barque-rigged auxiliary steam screw vessel" or "composite screw sloop". These descriptive phrases are reasonably self-explanatory, though since they have been taken from a wide range of sources they may not be totally consistent. In the case of naval vessels, I initially used Colledge's standard two volume text (1969 and 1970) on *Ships of the Royal Navy* for these type designations as well as for the linear dimensions and tonnages. However, in this area I have been extremely fortunate in having access to manuscript lists prepared by David Lyon of the National Maritime Museum for forthcoming publication. This has enabled me to provide not only more accurate type designations and armament figures, but also more accurate length, beam and tonnage measurements since Lyon's figures are taken from Admiralty plans and lists of dimensions. Where the figures I give differ from those of Colledge, this is the reason.

Linear dimensions

For each vessel I have tried to give some indication of the physical size in terms of a length and beam measurement. The length measurement for sailing vessels is roughly equivalent to the length between perpendiculars for steam vessels. The measurements have not been converted to their metric equivalents since the vessels would have been built to imperial specifications and such conversions would have little meaning.

Tonnage

Since tonnage is a very complex subject, confusing to many landsmen and mariners alike, a brief explanation may be useful.

First, despite the modern connotations of the word, tonnage was not historically a measure of weight, but rather of the carrying capacity of a vessel on the basis of which such charges as harbour dues and taxes were levied. Indeed, it is suggested that the term "tonnage" itself is derived from early measures in which the ability to carry *tuns* of wine was assessed. By an Act of Parliament in 1773 the tonnage measurement was standardised for British vessels into *Builders' Old Measurement*, using a formula based on the length and beam to calculate a volume which was then divided by a rather arbitrary figure of 94 (cubic feet) to give the final measure. This system remained in force until the advent of iron and steam propulsion totally changed the shape of ships and made it inappropriate. However, it continued to be used for all naval ships until 1873 and is indicated in this list by the letters (bm). Builders' measurement was replaced for naval vessels from 1873 by *displacement tonnage*, a true measurement of the weight of the ship and based on the volume of water displaced when afloat. An idea of the relationship between builders' measurement and displacement can be obtained from some of the entries for naval steam vessels which bridge this period and for which both measurements are given in the *Navy List*.

For merchant vessels the builders' measurement was replaced from the mid nineteenth century by a variety of measurements of which the following will be found in the list: *gross tonnage*, which is the total volume of the ship's hull in cubic feet below the upper deck, divided by 100; *net tonnage*, which is gross tonnage after deduction of non cargo carrying spaces such as crew's quarters, ship's stores, fuel bunkers, machinery spaces and so on; *deadweight tonnage*, which is a measure of the number of tons weight of cargo which the vessel can carry to trim her hull down to her allotted Plimsoll marks; *register tonnage*, which may be either the gross or net tonnage, since both figures appear on the vessel's certificate of registration. Finally, the tonnage of yachts is expressed as Thames Measurement, an index of capacity similar to builders' measurement introduced originally in 1855 by the Royal Thames Yacht Club to produce a fairer method of handicapping vessels. Further information on tonnage measurement will be found in Arnott *et al.* (1951), Hogg (1956), Barnaby (1960) and Kemp (1976).

Engine power

For powered vessels I have tried to give a figure for the engine's horse-power, a subject almost as confusing to the layman as is tonnage. As a convenient unit in which to measure the power of steam engines, the horse-power was introduced by James Watt, with one such unit being equivalent to 33,000 foot pounds per minute. Since Watt's engines were all designed to operate at the same boiler pressure and with a constant relationship between the piston speed and the length of stroke, he was able to use a simple formula to estimate the power that each engine would develop when at work. Since an engine was denominated as of such a power, this figure became known as the *nominal horse power* (n.h.p.). As boiler pressures and piston speeds increased, the power actually developed by engines exceeded the nominal horse power to an ever increasing extent. However, nominal horse power continued to be used, though from time to time modified in various ways, since it provides a better idea of the commercial value and size of an engine than does the developed power. Where a horse-power is given in the list without qualification (i.e. simply as h.p.) it may generally be assumed to refer to a nominal horse power.

Various methods were devised to measure the actual power developed by engines, but from the point of view of this list the only important one was that giving *indicated horse-power* (i.h.p.). This is defined as the measure of work done in the cylinder of a steam-engine and is named from the instrument, an indicator, used to measure the steam pressure in the cylinder.

Thus, for comparative purposes, the important distinction is simply that n.h.p. is a purely theoretical figure, while i.h.p. is an empirical one based on actual measurements.

Origin of vessel

Wherever possible the locality and date of building is given, sometimes with the name of the builder and of the first owner, where known. Where the building date is not known, the earliest date at which I am aware of the existence of the vessel is given, together with the context, such as purchase, transfer or charter.

Ship's name

The vessels are listed alphabetically under the name by which they were known during their oceanographic activities. Earlier or subsequent names are listed in the index. Vessels having the same name are arranged chronologically in the main list; where they appear in the index they are distinguished by their building date or other earliest date (e.g. "Investigator (purchased 1798)", "Investigator (built 1881)", "Investigator (built 1907)").

Personnel

For the oceanographic cruise or cruises of each vessel I have tried to provide the name of at least the principal scientist either participating in the voyage or requesting the gathered information. Where the identity of the vessel's commander was easily obtained or seemed significant, this is also given. However, where it seemed to me that the commander's identity is not particularly important, as, for instance, during the 1899 voyage of the cable vessel *Britannia,* I have made no significant effort to discover it.

The names of other participants in a particular voyage, whether mariners or scientists, are generally included only if they have some broader significance in the development of oceanography.

Scientific results

The amount of detail given for each cruise is extremely variable; in some cases a world voyage lasting two or three years is dismissed in a few lines, while several hundred words are sometimes devoted to a cruise of only a few weeks duration. In most cases such uneven divisions of effort and space are hopefully based on rational assessments of the overall relative importance of the voyages concerned. Such desirable objectivity, however, has undoubtedly been reduced both by the availability of published information and by my own specific interests. Consequently, biology probably receives more than its fair share of attention relative to the other scientific disciplines, while individual cruises, such as those of the *Isabella* in 1818 and of the *Bulldog* in 1860, perhaps also fare better than they should.

In an attempt to redress such in-built bias I have tried to put the main voyages into the overall context of the developing science, so that by reading the entries in chronological order a reader should obtain some idea of the progress of marine science in general and of British contributions to it in particular. On the other hand, the list does not pretend to offer more than a brief introduction to the history of oceanography which should be pursued further in the excellent treatments mentioned above, or in the primary sources referred to in the entries for individual vessels. Similarly, since progress in oceanography has frequently depended upon the availability of appropriate technology, I have often felt it necessary to mention the specific instruments employed on particular vessels. However, these references are mostly quite brief and for more information the reader is referred to the excellent recent treatment of the development of marine instrumentation by McConnell (1982).

Illustrations

I would have liked to provide an illustration of each of the vessels dealt with, particularly when I found that the Ray Society was prepared to support such a lavish treatment. Despite the generous assistance of the various sources of illustrations acknowledged elsewhere, I have had to settle for rather less than sixty per cent coverage in the time available. Despite this limitation, I hope that the drawings, paintings and photographs reproduced turn what would otherwise be a rather dull text into an attractive and emotive volume as a tribute to the many sailors and scientists who often made their contribution to the progress of oceanography under far from ideal conditions.

ALPHABETICAL LIST

ACTIVE

Wooden whaling barque, built Peterhead 1852, 117′ long, 28′6″ beam, 348 tons gross. After some years as a sailing vessel based in Peterhead, the *Active* was engined with a 40 h.p. auxiliary steam engine by Hall, Russell and Co. of Aberdeen, and was transferred to the Dundee Register in 1873 under the ownership of the Tay Whale Fishing Company.

The Dundee whaler Active *under sail in pack ice. Courtesy Dundee Museums and Art Galleries.*

In 1892-1893 the *Active* accompanied the *Balaena* to the Antarctic under the command of Captain Thomas Robertson, later to command the *Scotia* during the Scottish National Antarctic Expedition in 1902-04. During her antarctic cruise the *Active* was accompanied by C.W. Donald as naturalist.

After her return from the Antarctic the vessel continued to be employed in the Dundee whaling fleet until the outbreak of the First World War when she was employed by the Admiralty. She was lost off the Orkneys in 1915 en route for Russia with munitions.

References:
Donald, 1896; Henderson, Dundee Museum, pers. comm.

HMS ADVENTURE

"Aid" class transport, built Lynn 1809, 313 (bm), 104′ long, 26′ beam, 4-12 pdr carronades, 2-6 pdr carronades. Design complement 39, but only 10 as a survey vessel.

The *Adventure* was originally named the *Aid* and became a survey vessel in 1817 when she was sent out to the Mediterranean to be placed under the command of Capt. W.H. Smyth. The vessel was renamed *Adventure* in 1821 and continued to be used in surveys in the Mediterranean under Smyth until 1824. In 1820 he met the chemist Alexander Marcet who was anxious to obtain sub-surface water samples from the Mediterranean to investigate the suspected existence of an outflowing deep current in the Strait of Gibraltar. The presence of an eastward flowing surface current through the Strait was well established, but there was disagreement about whether the resulting excess water in the Mediterranean evaporated away or escaped in an undercurrent back into the Atlantic. Marcet had already examined several Mediterranean water samples, but the results were inconclusive. Smyth therefore undertook to obtain further samples in a sampler supplied by Marcet. Unfortunately, the latter died in 1822 while Smyth was still away and the resulting samples were mostly given away and used for purposes other than those which Marcet had in mind. The three remaining samples were examined by William Hyde Wollaston, who met Smyth in 1827. Wollaston reported that one of these samples, from a depth of 670 fathoms (1147m) within the Strait, had a salinity four times as great as normal sea water and he interpreted this as clear proof of the existence of an outflowing current of very dense water. Wollaston's result must have been due to the water sample evaporating during storage. The controversy about the Gibraltar undercurrent continued until its existence was clearly demonstrated by the observations carried out from the *Porcupine* and *Shearwater* in 1870 and 1871.

From 1826 to 1830 the *Adventure* was employed in survey work off the coasts of South America under the command of Capt. P.P. King and accompanied by the *Beagle,* eventually under Robert Fitzroy.

In 1839 the *Adventure* reverted to use as a transport and was sold in 1853.

References:
Day, 1967; Deacon, 1971; Fitzroy, 1839; Marcet, 1819; Wollaston, 1829.

ADVENTURE

170 ton schooner (previously the sealer *Unicorn*) purchased by Robert Fitzroy for £1,300 in March 1833 at the Falklands and fitted out at his own expense to accompany the *Beagle*. The ship was named by Fitzroy after the earlier *Adventure.* The Admiralty refused to reimburse Fitzroy for his expenses and he was therefore forced to sell the vessel at Valparaiso in November 1834. Nevertheless, Fitzroy made a small profit on the ship herself, since she fetched £1,400.

Reference:
Fitzroy, 1839.

HMS ALCESTE

5th rate, 28-18 pdr, 16-32 pdr carronades, 2-9 pdr, built Rochefort 1804, 1098 (bm), 152′5″ long, 40′ beam. The vessel was originally the French *La Minerve,* captured in 1806 by a British squadron off Rochefort.

In 1816 the *Alceste* sailed to China under the command of Capt. Murray Maxwell, in company with H.M.S. *Lyra,* carrying an embassy led by Lord Amherst. Clarke Abel, a protégé of Sir Joseph Banks, accompanied the embassy as doctor and naturalist, together with his brother-in-law as assistant and with a gardener from Kew. During the voyage through the Yellow Sea, Abel made many observations of the temperature of the sea at depths between 15 and 40 fathoms (27 and 72m), using a hollow brass cylinder with valves at top and bottom and with a Fahrenheit thermometer inside. During exploration of the China Seas while the embassy was ashore, Maxwell made a collection of madreporarian corals, while Capt. Basil Hall in the *Lyra* collected a variety of plants and marine animals. In February 1817, during the homeward voyage, the *Alceste* was wrecked when she struck a rock in the Straits of Gaspar in the East Indies and virtually all of the collections were lost, together with most of Abel's observations.

References:
Abel, 1818; Deacon, 1971; Gosset, 1986.

HMS ALERT

Screw sloop, 17-32 pdr, built Pembroke Dock 1856, 751 (bm), 1045 tons displacement, 160' long, 32' beam, 100 n.h.p., 381 i.h.p.

The *Alert* was converted to a survey vessel for the British Arctic Expedition of 1875-1876 together with the *Discovery,* and with the *Valorous* as transport.

After M'Clintock had returned in the *Fox* from the Arctic in 1859 with confirmation of abandonment of the *Erebus* and *Terror* by Sir John Franklin's ill-fated expedition of 1845-1848, a

H.M.S. Alert *cutting a dock in the previous season's ice in Dobbin Bay. Courtesy National Maritime Museum. Neg. no. B 3669 (D).*

long period of national disillusionment with Arctic exploration had ensued. However, successive Presidents of the Royal Geographical Society kept alive the interest in Polar exploration, and by the early 1870s the time seemed ripe for further British involvement.

Command of the Expedition was given to Capt. G.S. Nares who had visited the Arctic on Capt. Henry Kellett's unsuccessful search for Franklin in 1852 and had subsequently surveyed in Australian waters, in the Mediterranean and the Red Sea in command of the *Salamander, Newport* and *Shearwater*. As the Arctic Expedition was being planned, Nares was commanding the *Challenger;* he was recalled in late 1874, along with Lieut. Pelham Aldrich who was to act as First Lieutenant in the *Alert*.

The main objective was to reach the North Pole via Smith Sound through which the U.S.S. *Polaris* had sailed and wintered in Polaris Bay in 1871-72. Scientific observations assumed a distinctly secondary role, and by far the most important oceanographic observations resulting from the expedition were those made from the transport, *Valorous*. All of the scientific work on the *Alert* and *Discovery* was originally to have been undertaken by naval officers, but two civilian naturalists, H.W. Feilden and C. Hart, were eventually appointed.

The vessels left Portsmouth in late May 1875 and reached Smith Sound in August. The *Discovery* wintered at Discovery Harbour, Lady Franklin Bay, while the *Alert* proceeded to 82°27′N, a higher latitude than any vessel had previously reached, and remained ice-bound off Cape Sheridan from September 1875 to July 1876.

During the winter, extensive meteorological observations and detailed measurements of total magnetic force, horizontal force and dip were made at both winter quarters. Frequent magnetic disturbances were correlated at both stations, and subsequently identified with similar disturbances recorded at the Kew Observatory. However, the expected correlation between

Officers of H.M.S. Alert *for the Arctic Expedition. Nares is in the centre, with Aldrich to his left (holding something) and Markham half seated beside him, Fielden is seated on the extreme right. Courtesy National Maritime Museum. Neg. no. D 949.*

such storms and the occurrence of auroras was not substantiated.

In the spring and summer of 1876 sledge parties left both the *Alert* and the *Discovery* to explore and chart the neighbouring coasts and to make geological, magnetic, and biological observations. One of these sledge parties, under Cdr. A.H. Markham and Lieut. A.C.C. Parr, went northwards towards the pole and reached a furthest point north of 83°20′26″.

Scurvy broke out in May 1876 and became increasingly serious during the summer until Nares eventually decided to end the expedition prematurely, leaving the winter quarters in August and reaching England in late October, six months after the return of the *Challenger* Expedition.

A committee of enquiry into the conduct of the expedition partly blamed Nares for the outbreak of scurvy. However, Nares received support from a number of eminent men, including Sir G.H. Richards the previous Hydrographer, and was once more given command of the *Alert* for surveying work in South American waters and in the southern Pacific. Since extensive deep sounding work was to be carried out, Nares was provided with the Lucas sounding machine for its first naval trial. The machine had been developed by Francis Lucas, Chief Engineer of the Telegraph Construction and Maintenance Company, and its use was recommended by Richards, by then the company's managing director. For the deep soundings Nares also took Baillie rods and *Bulldog* clams.

The *Alert* sailed from Plymouth in September 1878 via Madeira, St Vincent, Montevideo and the Falkland Islands, reaching the Strait of Magellan on New Year's Day 1879. Throughout 1879 and the first half of 1880 the *Alert* surveyed the coast of Patagonia, Nares being recalled and replaced by Capt. J.L.P. Maclear, his second-in-command on the *Challenger,* in spring 1879.

Leaving South America in June 1880, the *Alert* sailed via Tahiti and Fiji to Sydney, arriving in January 1881. After six months surveying off the eastern and northern coasts of Australia the ship sailed to Singapore for a refit where she was ordered to survey the Amirante and neighbouring islands in the south-western Indian Ocean. These surveys were conducted between March and May 1882 and the *Alert* then returned to England via South Africa, St. Helena and the Azores, arriving at Plymouth in September.

Throughout the voyage, shallow water dredging, townetting and other biological collecting was undertaken, mainly as a result of the efforts of Staff Surgeon R.W. Coppinger who sailed as scientist on this voyage and had been the Surgeon during the Arctic Expedition. The resulting collection was presented to the British Museum (Natural History) and was so extensive that the Trustees sanctioned the publication of a special volume to carry the reports on it.

In 1885 and 1886 the *Alert* made further visits to the Arctic when she was lent to the Canadian Government to improve the navigational knowledge of Hudson Strait. She was officered and manned by the Canadian Government but was accompanied in 1886 by A.H. Markham who had also participated in the 1876 expedition.

The *Alert* was sold in 1896.

References:
Coppinger, 1883, 1884; Deacon and Savours, 1976; Hattersley-Smith, 1976; Markham, 1888; McConnell, 1982; Nares, 1878; Ritchie, 1967.

ALEXANDER

British 252 ton whaler hired by the Admiralty to search for the North-West Passage in 1818. She was the first command of W.E. Parry.
For further details see *Isabella.*

ALEXANDER, 250 Tons. 35 Men.
Lieu.ᵗ Wᵐ EDWᵈ PARRY, Commander.

ISABELLA, 382 Tons. 47 Men.
Captain JOHN ROSS.

DOROTHEA, 370 Tons. 47 Men.
Captain DAVID BUCHAN.

TRENT. 250 Tons. 35 Men.
Lieu.ᵗ JNᵒ FRANKLIN, Commander.

PORTRAITS of the VESSELS on the POLAR EXPEDITION of 1818.

The projecting timbers are for hoisting up the Boats to: but in bad weather they are got on board and laid upon the cross pieces, bottom upward, from bow to stern. The projections are placed two between the fore and main masts, one between the main and mizen, and one at the stern

Published April 21ˢᵗ 1818 by Jⁿ Whittle and Rᵈ H. Laurie Nᵒ.53 Fleet Street London

Vessels of the 1818 Polar Expedition. H.M.S. Alexander, Isabella, Dorothea *and* Trent. *Courtesy National Maritime Museum. Neg. no. 8856.*

AURORA

Barque-rigged whaler built Dundee 1876, 386 registered tons, 165′ long, 30′ beam, used for the Australian Antarctic Expedition under the leadership of Douglas Mawson from 1911 to 1914. The Expedition was financed by Australian funding, both private and public, but was also supported by a contribution of £2,000 from the British Government.

For the first 34 years of her existence the *Aurora* had served entirely in northern waters, initially in the Dundee whaling fleet and later in the Newfoundland sealing trade. In 1881 she was apparently fitted with an engine and a twin bladed propellor (replaced by a 4-bladed propellor for the Antarctic expedition), and had participated in the relief of the Greely Expedition in 1884.

The main objective of Mawson's expedition was to explore the Australasian Antarctic segment, that is from Cape Adare westward to Gaussberg, and for the shore parties to make magnetic and other scientific observations. In addition, the expedition vessel was to make oceanographic observations during the voyages to deliver and relieve the shore parties and during short sub-antarctic cruises in the intervening periods.

The *Aurora* was commanded by John King Davis who also supervised her refit in the South West India Docks in London in preparation for the expedition. Amongst the modifications at this time she was given a new foremast and re-rigged as a barquentine. She was also fitted with two sounding machines, one of them driven by an engine originally built for the Scottish National Antarctic Expedition in the *Scotia* and lent to Mawson by W.S. Bruce.

Aurora. *Courtesy National Maritime Museum. Neg. no. P722.*

The *Aurora* sailed from London on 28 July 1911 to be joined by Mawson and most of the expedition members when she reached Tasmania.

Finally she left Hobart on 2 December, with a ship's complement of 25, together with the shore party members, the remaining personnel being carried to Macquarie Island on the S.S. *Toroa,* hired as a tender to the *Aurora.*

At Macquarie Island a shore party was landed under G.F. Ainsworth. This party was to spend 23 months on the island and make the first detailed investigation of it.

The *Aurora* sailed on Christmas Day 1911 with the intention of establishing three separate antarctic bases. In the event only two bases were established, a main one under Mawson at Commonwealth Bay in Adelie Land, and a smaller one under Frank Wild on the Shackleton Ice Shelf, before the ship returned to Hobart on March 12. Here Davis met Amundsen in the *Fram* on his return from the successful attempt on the South Pole.

The *Aurora* was refitted at Sydney in preparation for a winter cruise to carry out deep-sea work during which she was joined by E.R. Waite, Curator of the Canterbury Museum, as biologist. For deep sea trawling the ship was furnished with Monegasque (Agassiz) trawls and 3000 fathoms (5847m) of tapered steel wire. The wire was stored on a reel which was driven by a chain drive from a cargo winch, but the warp was hauled in with a steam windlass fitted in Sydney.

The ship left Sydney on 20 May and sailed via Macquarie Island and the Auckland Islands to Lyttelton, New Zealand where she arrived on 11 July, finally returning to Melbourne for a refit on 17 August 1912. The oceanographic results of this cruise were very limited, mainly

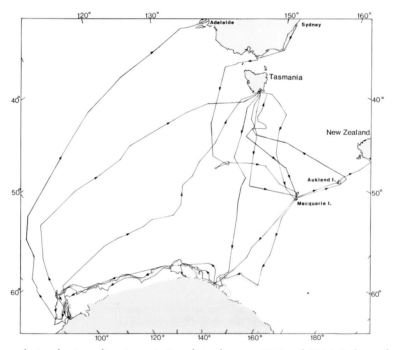

Tracks of the Aurora *during the Australian Antarctic Expedition between 1911 and 1914. Redrawn from Mawson, 1915.*

because bad weather prevented the extensive use of the trawl, but several deep-sea soundings were obtained to depths of about 2500 fathoms (4573m), particularly in the reported neighbourhood of the Royal Company Islands where no evidence of land was obtained.

While the *Aurora* was refitting, Davis had the opportunity to participate in a cruise of the Commonwealth Fisheries Investigation vessel *Endeavour* during which he was able to see deep sea gear being used. (The *Endeavour* eventually disappeared with all hands, including H.C. Dannevig, the Director of the Commonwealth Fisheries, during a passage from Macquarie

Island to Hobart in December 1914.)

After moving from Melbourne to Tasmania the *Aurora* undertook a second sub-antarctic cruise from Hobart via Macquarie Island and the Auckland Islands and back to Hobart between 12 November and 14 December. The "guest" biologist on this cruise was T. Flynn (Errol Flynn's father) from Hobart University. The trawl was used on five occasions but was successful only twice. However, as on the earlier cruises, extensive sounding work was carried out, including the discovery of an area of shallow water about 200 miles south of Tasmania later named the Mill Rise by Mawson after H.R. Mill.

The ship was now prepared for an antarctic voyage to relieve the shore parties and left Hobart on 26 December. The main base at Commonwealth Bay was reached on 13 January 1913 where it was learned that three sledging parties were still out. Two of these parties had returned safely by 18 January, leaving Mawson still missing, together with his companions X. Mertz and B.E.S. Ninnis. Davis searched unsuccessfully for Mawson's party along the coast to the eastward from 29-31 January and finally left Commonwealth Bay to relieve Wild's western party on 8 February, leaving five of the main base party for a second winter and to search for the missing men.

Later the same day Davis received a radio message from the base that Mawson had arrived, but that both Mertz and Ninnis were dead. Davis could not himself communicate with the base since the *Aurora* carried no transmitter! Bad weather prevented the vessel from relieving the main base and Davis abandoned the attempt on 9 February, successfully collecting the western party on 23 February and returning to Hobart on 15 March. Here they heard that the *Terra Nova* had arrived in New Zealand the previous month with the tragic news of Scott's Expedition.

The *Aurora* was laid up while Davis travelled to London and then back to Australia to raise funds for a relief expedition. This accomplished, after considerable difficulty, the *Aurora* was refitted at Melbourne and finally sailed from Hobart on 19 November 1913 for her third antarctic voyage.

Ainsworth's team at Macquarie Island was taken off, responsibility for maintaining the wireless station passing to the Commonwealth Government. (It was after relieving this station the following year that the *Endeavour* was lost.) The *Aurora* now sailed direct to Commonwealth Bay and had taken aboard Mawson's party, together with the dogs and equipment, by Christmas Eve. To employ the remainder of the season profitably the ship sailed westward, along the edge of the pack ice, as far as 90°E and investigated the Shackleton Ice Shelf off Queen Mary Island before returning to Adelaide on 26 February 1914.

This final antarctic voyage was much more productive oceanographically than the earlier ones, for in addition to the soundings and dredge and trawl hauls several temperature sections were obtained with Ekman reversing bottles fitted with Richter thermometers.

The scientific results appeared in a long series of official reports published by the Australian Government Printing Office between 1916 and 1947. The bulk of these dealt with the biological material which was distributed to specialists after the expedition by W.A. Haswell of the University of Sydney, but one of the potentially most interesting groups, the hexactinellid sponges, was lost in transit to Prof. I. Ijima in Tokyo.

In 1914 the *Aurora* was employed under the command of A.E. Mackintosh to transport the Ross Sea Party of Shackleton's Imperial Transantarctic Expedition. This party was to establish a series of depots south to the base of the Beardmore Glacier to be used by Shackleton's planned sledge party on their journey from the Weddell Sea where they were to have been landed from the *Endurance.*

Having landed ten members ashore at Cape Evans on Ross Island, including Mackintosh who was lost with two others in the Ross Sea area, the *Aurora* broke away from her moorings on 6 May 1915 and drifted in pack ice until March 1916 by which time she had travelled some 1200 miles along the coasts of South Victoria Land and Oates Land. During the drift the vessel was under the command of J.R. Stenhouse.

After refitting, the *Aurora* returned to the Ross Sea in the following season, now under the command of J.K. Davis once more and with Shackleton aboard, and rescued the surviving members of the Cape Evans party in January 1917.

Having had such a colourful career in polar waters, spanning some forty years, the *Aurora* was finally lost on what should have been a routine commercial voyage. She sailed from Sydney on 20 June 1917 bound for Iquique, Chile, with a cargo of coal. The ship failed to arrive at her destination and was finally posted as missing at Lloyds on 2 January 1918.

References:

Davis, 1919; Lindsay, 1911; Mawson, 1915; Wordie, 1921.

BAFFIN

Whaler built 1820 by Mottershead and Hays, Liverpool, 55 tons burthen.

William Scoresby Jnr. had a one third share in the ship and made his last four voyages to the Greenland whale fishery in it from 1820 to 1824. During these voyages he continued his earlier oceanographic observations made in the *Resolution* and the *Esk*. For further details see under *Esk*.

References:

Scoresby, 1823; Stamp and Stamp, 1976.

BALAENA

Wooden barque, built Drammen, Norway 1872 as the *Mjølnev*, 141′ long, 31′ beam, 416 tons gross, 66 h.p. auxiliary engine.

The Dundee whaler Balaena. *Courtesy City of Hull Museums.*

The *Balaena* was added to the Dundee register in 1891 under the ownership of R. Kinnes and made one whaling trip to Greenland before she was used under the command of Capt. Alexander Fairweather for an Antarctic expedition in 1892-1893 to investigate the potential whale and seal fisheries of the Southern Ocean. The *Balaena* was accompanied by three other whalers, the *Active, Diana* and *Polar Star*.

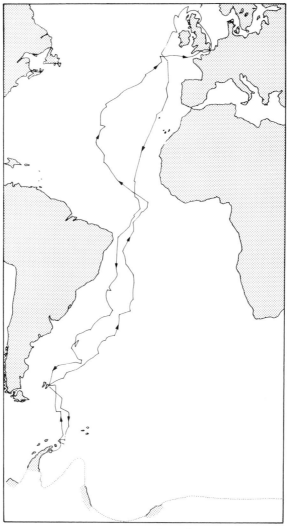

Track of the Balaena *Expedition to the Antarctic in 1892-93, redrawn from Brown, Mossman and Pirie, 1906. More detailed tracks of the* Balaena *and* Active *around the Graham Land peninsula are given in Bruce, 1896.*

William Spiers Bruce, later to lead the Scottish National Antarctic Expedition on board the *Scotia*, sailed on the *Balaena* as naturalist.

Although the aims of the expedition were primarily commercial, the vessels were supplied with a variety of equipment for biological and hydrographic work by individual scientists, while the Royal Geographical Society and the Meteorological Office provided instruments for geographical and meteorological observations. Because of the emphasis on the search for whales and seals, little biological sampling was achieved, but extensive meteorological and surface sea temperature observations were made.

After her return from the Antarctic the *Balaena* was employed as a Dundee whaler until the end of the First World War, for several years being commanded by Thomas Robertson, who had been captain of the *Active* during the antarctic voyage.

BRITISH OCEANOGRAPHIC VESSELS

After the war, the *Balaena* was owned by the Kymo Shipping Company until 1929 when she was sold as a hulk.

References:
Bruce, 1896; Donald, 1896; Henderson, Dundee Museum, pers. comm.; Murdoch, 1894

HMS BEACON

"Hecla" class bomb vessel, built Pembroke Dock 1823, 378 (bm), 106' long, 27' beam. The *Beacon* was originally launched as the *Meteor* and her name was changed in 1832, presumably to distinguish her from the steam vessel of the same name built in 1824 (see under *Lightning*). Nevertheless, there was a period from 1828, when the steam vessel entered the Navy List, until 1832 during which there were two *Meteors* in commission at the same time!

The vessel was employed in surveying in the Mediterranean under the command of Cdr. R. Copeland from 1830 to 1836 when her command was taken by Thomas Graves until, eventually, she was sold for £1,500 in Malta in 1846.

The *Beacon* is best known in the history of oceanography for the period in 1841 and 1842 during which the Manx naturalist Edward Forbes was aboard the vessel and carried out dredging in the Aegean. Forbes' results led to the formulation of his "Azoic theory" which dominated deep-sea biology until the cruises of the *Lightning* and *Porcupine* in the late 1860s and early 1870s.

By the time he joined the *Beacon*, Forbes' interest in deep dredging was well established. In his youth he had collected intensively around the coasts of his native Isle of Man and had continued his interests in marine biology when he went to Edinburgh to study medicine in 1831 at the age of 16. Although he never took his medical examinations, he stayed on in Edinburgh throughout the 1830s, but making various visits to Europe to study natural history. In 1839 he had dredged around the Orkneys and Shetland with John Goodsir and had presented the results at the British Association meeting that year. This report was largely instrumental in the establishment of the Association's Dredging Committee which stimulated extensive marine collecting around the British coasts during the succeeding four decades.

Forbes had attempted, unsuccessfully, to obtain a permanent post in natural history when he heard that Graves was looking for a naturalist to join the *Beacon*. Forbes was offered the post, enthusiastically accepted it, and travelled to Malta with his naturalist friend William Thompson to join the vessel in April 1841. Thompson returned home in less than two months, but Forbes remained with the *Beacon* for 18 months.

Forbes fitted in very well on the ship, becoming popular with both the officers and the men. He made extensive shore excursions, including a period of several months ashore in Asia Minor with Thomas Spratt, the *Beacon's* First Lieutenant. Spratt was later to command the *Spitfire* and *Medina* and to become deeply involved in the development of techniques for obtaining deep-sea soundings. During these excursions Forbes made important terrestrial and coastal marine collections, but by far his most important work was the 100 or so dredge hauls made down to a depth of some 230 fathoms (420m). These were made largely from the *Beacon's* tenders, the *Fanny* and the rather larger *Isabella*, first under the command of Spratt and later under Richard Hoskyn, the Master of the *Beacon* (see also *Porcupine*).

After his long period ashore during which one of his companions, E.T. Daniell, had died of fever, Forbes heard that his father had suffered severe financial losses and would therefore be unable to give his son further monetary support. However, Forbes had already decided to extend his marine work to the Red Sea for comparison with his Aegean results and had been awarded funds from the British Association and the Geological Society to enable him to do this. In the event, he heard that the chair of botany at King's College was vacant and he left the *Beacon* in October 1842 to return to London to secure the position.

The bulk of the dredging results were never published, for in the years leading up to his early death in 1854 Forbes was severely overworked, first by having to take the job of Curator of the Geological Society in addition to his professorship, and later as the first full-time palaeontologist of the Geological Survey. Nevertheless, in a "Report on the Mollusca and Radiata [roughly the coelenterates and echinoderms] of the Aegean Sea", presented to the 1843 meeting of the British Association, he summarised his current views on animal distribution and introduced his Azoic theory.

From his earlier dredging work in British waters he had described four zones of animal life from the littoral zone between the tide marks to his deepest zone, the region of deep-sea corals, from 50 fathoms (90m) to beyond 100 fathoms. From the Aegean results Forbes recognised eight zones, the deepest, from 105 fathoms (192m) to the greatest depth dredged (230 fathoms, 420m), showing decrease in both the numbers of species and of individuals with increasing depth and "...pointing to a zero in the distribution of animal life as yet unvisited."

In subsequent papers (Forbes 1844(b), 1846) and also in *The Natural History of European Seas,* completed by Robert Godwin-Austin and published after Forbes' death, his views on the distribution of marine organisms were amplified and extended. Many of his conclusions have survived almost unchanged, but the one for which he is usually remembered, and which had the greatest influence over marine biology for almost 30 years, was his belief that the bulk of the sea-floor, beyond about 300 fathoms (550m), would be found to be totally devoid of life. Despite the accumulation of evidence arguing against the Azoic Theory, including John Ross's retrieval of a starfish supposedly from about 1000 fathoms on the *Isabella* in 1818, Wallich's similar experience on the *Bulldog* in 1860, James Clark Ross's deep dredgings from the *Erebus* and *Terror* in 1839 to 1843, and the discovery of animals attached to the submarine cable between Sardinia and Bona retrieved for repair in 1860, the theory was not considered to have been disproved finally until the cruises of the *Lightning* and *Porcupine* in 1868 and 1869.

References:

Deacon, 1978; Forbes 1844(a), 1844(b), 1846; Mills, 1978, 1984; Rehbock, 1979.

HMS BEAGLE

"Cherokee" class brig-sloop, built Woolwich Dockyard 1820, c. 236 (bm), 90' long, 25' beam. The *Beagle* was one of 115 similar vessels laid down between 1807 and 1830.

Having been rigged originally as a brig, the vessel was barque-rigged, with a mizen mast added, in preparation for her first South American voyage. In this first voyage, from 1826-1830, the *Beagle* accompanied H.M.S. *Adventure* under the command of Capt. P.P. King and was commanded originally by Commander Stokes. When Stokes committed suicide, Robert Fitzroy was placed in command from 13 November 1829.

Beagle's second voyage to South America, from 1831 to 1836 and again under the command of Fitzroy, is much better known since this is the cruise in which Charles Darwin participated as naturalist and companion to Fitzroy. Darwin's observations, particularly in the Galapagos, led him to his theory of natural selection and ultimately to the publication of the *Origin of Species.*

Fitzroy made extensive observations of tides in the Pacific, while Darwin collected many biological samples in shallow water and developed his ideas on the origin and development of coral reefs. However, virtually no true oceanographic observations were made from the *Beagle.* Nevertheless, the influence of Darwin's evolutionary theory on all aspects of biology

H.M.S. Beagle *in the Galapagos 2.15p.m. on 17th October 1835. Artist J. Chancellor. Reproduced by kind permission of Alexander Gallery Publications and Mrs R.M. Chancellor.*

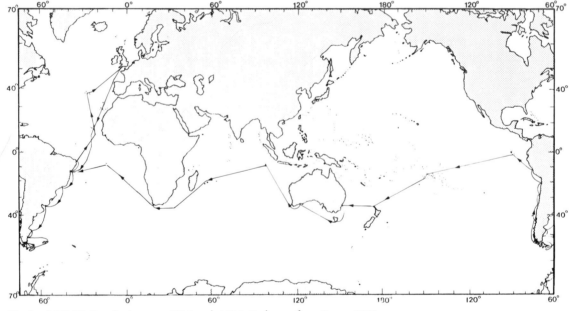

Track of H.M.S. Beagle *between 1831 and 1836. Redrawn from Brent, 1961.*

ensure the importance of the *Beagle* in the development of oceanography.

The *Beagle* was employed in surveying in Australian waters from 1837 to 1843, initially under J.C. Wickham and later under J.L. Stokes. In 1846 she became a customs watch vessel, was designated WV7 in 1863 and was sold in 1870.

References:

Brent, 1981; Fitzroy, 1836, 1839; Darling, 1978; Darwin, 1859.

HMS BLOSSOM

Ship sloop, 16-32 pdr carronades, 8-18 pdr carronades, 2-6 pdr, built by Guillaume, Northam 1806, 423 (bm), 108'4" long, 29'7" beam, design complement 125.

The *Blossom* became an exploration vessel in 1825 and was used for a circumnavigation from 1825 to 1828 under the command of Capt. Frederick William Beechey. Beechey was instructed to visit Bering Strait to await the arrival of either Parry's expedition in the *Hecla* and *Fury* (q.v.) or John Franklin's British Arctic Land Expedition, should either of them succeed in penetrating from the east. Accordingly, Beechey visited the Strait in both 1826 and 1827 finding no sign of either of the other parties though his mate, Thomas Elson, reached Point Barrow and came within 250km of the furthest point reached by Franklin.

During the arctic voyages Beechey made numerous measurements of surface temperature and regularly determined the specific gravity. Deep sea temperatures were obtained with self-registering but unprotected thermometers, mostly in the upper 300 fathoms (549m) but with four sets of serial observations to as deep as 850 fathoms (1555m).

The *Blossom* was classed as a survey ship in 1829, became a hulk at Sheerness in 1833 and was broken up in 1848.

References:
Beechey, 1831; Deacon, 1971.

HMS BRAMBLE

"Bramble" class cutter, 2-brass 6 pdr, 8-12 pdr carronades, built Plymouth Dockyard 1822, 161 (bm), 70'9" long, 24'2.5" beam, design complement 50. The vessel was converted to a schooner-rigged survey ship in 1842.

H.M.S. Bramble. Artist W. Knell. Courtesy National Maritime Museum. Neg. no. 9300.

Under the command of Lieut. C.B. Yule, H.M.S. *Bramble* was used as a tender to H.M.S. *Fly* during Francis Blackwood's surveying voyage in the south-western Pacific from 1842 to 1845.   The *Bramble* remained in the south-western Pacific, still under Yule's command, as tender to H.M.S. *Rattlesnake,* until Capt. Stanley's death in March 1850 when Yule was appointed in his place and brought the *Rattlesnake* back to England.

The *Bramble* was lent to the Colonial Department in 1853 as a diving-bell vessel at Sydney and was sold in 1876 as a lightship.

Reference:

MacGillivray, 1852.

BRITANNIA

Twin-screw cable vessel built by Laird Brothers of Birkenhead in 1885, 859 tons net, 1525 tons gross, 247' long, 34' beam, 180 h.p.

The *Britannia* was originally built for the Telegraph Construction and Maintenance Company and was sold to the Eastern Telegraph Company in 1904.   The *Britannia* became a cable hulk in Zanzibar in 1924 and was sold for scrap in 1934.

In 1899, when she still belonged to the Telegraph Construction and Maintenance Company, the *Britannia* surveyed cable routes between Europe and North America under the supervision of R.E. Peake.

Two new routes were proposed, one from Germany to New York and a second from Ireland to Nova Scotia, both via the Azores.   The *Britannia* therefore carried out extensive soundings

Cable ship Britannia. *Courtesy Cammell Laird Shipbuilders Ltd.*

on the Azores Bank and also on lines from the Azores to New York, Nova Scotia back to the Azores, then to the coast of Ireland and finally from the Azores to the mouth of the Channel.

A total of some 477 soundings were taken, most of them including samples of the bottom sediment which were reported on by John Murray in an appendix to Peake's general account of the cruise. Bottom temperatures were measured at 150 localities and many calculations of the surface currents were made on the basis of the set experienced by the ship during the 6700 mile voyage.

On the track between the mouth of the Channel and the Azores, two soundings of over 3000 fathoms (5487m) were obtained at about 43°N: 20°W in a depression which was named the Peake Deep. In the 1960s a second deep, slightly to the south-east of the first, was discovered from R.R.S. *Discovery*. This depression was named the Freen deep, the two names together alluding to a well-known manufacturer of biscuits, which are an indispensible element of all modern oceanographic cruises. Since Peake's name was spelt slightly differently from that of the manufacturer, the second name was also intentionally mis-spelt. Of the names Huntly and Palmer, given to the the ridges separating the Peake and Freen Deeps and so-named for a rival manufacturer, only the second still remains.

References:
Baglehole, 1969; Haigh, 1968; Matthew *et al,* 1969; Peake, 1901.

BUCCANEER

Screw cable vessel built by Wigham Richardson and Co., Newcastle, 1885, 460 tons net, 785 tons gross, 190′ long, 28′ beam, 180 h.p., belonging to the India-Rubber, Gutta-Percha and Telegraph Works Company and employed largely in the Atlantic from 1885 to 1906.

Under the command of A.S. Thomson the vessel was accompanied in 1885-1886 by J.Y. Buchanan, the chemist during the *Challenger* Expedition, and John Rattray, a chemist on the staff of the newly opened Scottish Marine Station, during a sounding voyage from the Cape Verdes to equatorial Africa and Ascension Island. In addition to the soundings, observations of surface and submarine temperatures and currents were made and plankton samples obtained.

However, the most important discovery during the cruise was of an easterly flowing equatorial undercurrent beneath the westerly flowing southern equatorial surface current. This was revealed when great difficulty was experienced in obtaining soundings between 13°W and 16°W no matter how heavy a weight was used. Finally, Buchanan suspended a drogue some 50 metres beneath a surface float and found that it was carried eastward, against the surface current.

The validity of Buchanan's interpretation was questioned by Krummel (1910, 1911) and the undercurrent disappeared from the literature until it was rediscovered in the Pacific in 1952 and in the Atlantic in 1959.

The vessel was wrecked in 1914.

References:
Buchanan, 1887, 1888; Deacon, 1971; Haigh, 1968; Hisard, 1983, 1986; Krummel, 1910, 1911; Matthaus, 1969; Thomson, A. 1896.

HMS BULLDOG

"Bulldog" class paddle sloop, built Chatham Dockyard 1845, 1124 (bm), 190′ long, 35′8″ beam with 500 h.p. engines. In 1860 the *Bulldog* was employed in a sounding voyage to survey the deep-sea portions of a proposed northern route for the transatlantic telegraph cable via Greenland, Iceland and the Faröes, while the inshore sections were surveyed by the *Fox.*

The *Bulldog* voyage grew out of the interest in laying submarine cables during the 1840s and 1850s. Eventually, the cable was laid along the more direct route between Ireland and Newfoundland, surveyed by both British and American naval vessels during the 1850s (see, for instance, H.M.S. *Cyclops*). But after the failure of the first cable, laid by the U.S.S. *Niagara* and H.M.S. *Agamemnon* in 1858, the more northerly route, with shorter marine sections, received a good deal of commercial support. Accordingly, the promoters of this route approached the British Government and obtained agreement that the Admiralty would survey the deep-sea sections of the route while the telegraph company would take responsibility for the shallow-water sections.

The Royal Naval officer with the most experience of deep sounding was Lieut. Joseph Dayman, who had already carried out extensive surveys in the *Cyclops, Gorgon* and *Firebrand,* but he was passed over in favour of Capt. Sir Leopold M'Clintock. This was possibly because of M'Clintock's considerable Arctic experience, but the choice was also certainly influenced by the fact that he was a national figure since his return from his Arctic voyage in the *Fox* in 1859 with news of the fate of Sir John Franklin's expedition in the *Erebus* and *Terror.* On the recommendation of Sir Roderick Murchison and T.H. Huxley, the post of naturalist during the voyage was given to George Charles Wallich who had recently (1857) been invalided out of the Indian Army after a career as a surgeon.

H.M.S. Bulldog *entering Kidge Bay bearing news of the declaration of war with Russia by England. Artist Dutton. Courtesy National Maritime Museum. Neg. no. A 2478.*

For conventional soundings, in which no attempt was made to obtain samples of the sea-floor sediments, M'Clintock took 75,000 fathoms (about 85 miles) of light cod-line and large numbers of lead weights. For obtaining seabed samples, Brooke's sounding apparatus was used as modified for Dayman's cruise on the *Cyclops* in 1857. Sediment samples were rarely successfully brought back to the surface with this apparatus and a new instrument, the *Bulldog* clam, was therefore devised aboard. This instrument was based loosely on Ross's clam, constructed during the voyage of the *Isabella* in 1818, but in the *Bulldog* version the jaws were closed by a rubber band after the detachable weights had been released (see McConnell,

1982).   Wallich also took a small dredge, but he had insufficient rope to dredge in deep water and, in any case, he lost this instrument and a replacement made by the *Bulldog's* Chief Engineer after only one successful haul.

M'Clintock surveyed successfully the route from the Faröes via Iceland and Greenland to Labrador and back to the west coast of Greenland, recording his greatest depth, 2032 fathoms (3700m), between Greenland and Labrador.   On rounding Cape Farewell from west to east he encountered a great deal of ice and decided to survey the direct route to Rockall, avoiding Iceland.   During this passage the *Bulldog* experienced very bad weather and eventually had to run into Reykjavik after all to repair the storm damage.   Nevertheless, the four soundings which were obtained before the run to Iceland were, for Wallich, the most important of the voyage.

First, they ranged from 748 to 1620 fathoms (1360-2950m) in an area where they expected at least 2000 fathoms (3640m).   Much more significant, during the last sounding, at a depth of 1260 fathoms (2293m), the sounding line came back with thirteen brittlestars entangled in the lower part of it.

Because of the many problems associated with cable laying in Arctic waters and particularly the vulnerability of the cable in the shallow regions close to the shore, M'Clintock's survey was not ultimately used for the purpose for which it was intended.   Wallich, however, publicised the results widely because he felt that they disproved Edward Forbes' Azoic theory (see under *Beacon*) according to which little or no life existed at depths exceeding about 300 fathoms.   Wallich identified the brittlestars taken on the sounding line as a species otherwise known only from depths less than about 200 fathoms, believing that the unexpected shallow area from which they were obtained represented the submerged legendary "Land of Buss" of the old navigators, so that the brittlestars could have become acclimatized to deep-sea conditions as the area had slowly sunk during historical times.

Wallich's results, and the similar experience of John Ross during the *Isabella* cruise of 1818, were treated as circumstantial evidence for the existence of life at great depth.   The credit for finally disproving the azoic theory was ultimately given to Wyville Thomson and Carpenter for their dredging results from the *Lightning* and *Porcupine* in the late 1860s and early 1870s.   This greatly incensed Wallich and led to almost 40 years of bitterness in which he attempted to obtain the public recognition which he felt that he justly deserved for this and other discoveries.

The *Bulldog* was eventually destroyed while attacking a rebel steamer, the *Valorogue,* in Haiti in 1865.

References:
Gosset, 1986; M'Clintock, 1861; McConnell, 1982; Rice, Burstyn & Jones, 1976; Wallich, 1862.

HMS CASTLEREAGH

Schooner, 93 (bm).

The *Castlereagh* was purchased at Sydney in 1845 to act as a tender, together with H.M.S. *Bramble,* to H.M.S. *Fly* under Capt. Blackwood.   On the *Fly's* return to England in 1845 the *Castlereagh,* under the command of Lieut. D. Aird, was transferred to the *Rattlesnake* (Capt. Stanley) but she proved to be unfit for surveying and was sold back to her former owner about 1848.

Reference:
MacGillivray, 1852.

HMS CHALLENGER

"Pearl" class wooden steam-assisted screw corvette, 20-8inch, 2-68 pdr, built Woolwich 1858, 1462 (bm), 2306 tons displacement, 226' long overall, 200' length on deck, 40'6" beam, 400 n.h.p., 1234 i.h.p., normal complement 290.

The three and a half year voyage of H.M.S. *Challenger* from December 1872 to May 1876 has frequently been referred to as marking the birth of oceanography and has made the ship the most famous oceanographic vessel of them all. Consequently, more has been written about the *Challenger* than about any similar vessel, but the literature contains so many inconsistencies and inaccuracies that the details given here for the vessel herself demand some explanation.

H.M.S. Challenger *at St. Thomas, West Indies, March 1873. Courtesy British Museum (Natural History). During her eight day stay at St. Thomas the* Challenger *went to the assistance of a British merchant vessel, the* Varuna, *abandoned two months previously and brought to the Virgin Islands by a skeleton crew from another British ship, the* Roundtree. *These men were initially distrustful of the* Challenger, *thinking that by accepting assistance they might lose their salvage bounty.*

The ship was officially described as a steam corvette, but she was definitely primarily a sailing vessel, carrying over 16000 square feet of sails even after her spars had been reduced for her oceanographic voyage. Her steam engine was coupled to a twin-bladed screw which could be disconnected from the shaft and raised through a well passing through the main deck to reduce the resistance when the ship was under sail. Various figures for the power of the engines have appeared in the literature, including a surprising 4000 h.p. from W.J.J. Spry, a Sub.-Lieut. in the engineering department!

The vessel's length is variously given as between 200 and 226 feet and her beam as between 30 feet and 40 feet 6 inches. From her plans, drawn for her refit for the oceanographic voyage and reproduced in Linklater (1972), it is clear that the shorter length was "between perpendiculars" and the larger figure refers to her "overall" length. Similarly, her beam was clearly about 40 feet.

As explained in the introduction, the tonnage measurement of naval vessels was changed in

1873 from builder's old measure to displacement. The *Challenger* was one of those vessels whose service bridged this change so that the Navy List gives both figures which seem to have been quoted indiscriminately and without explanation in the literature.

Finally, various figures have been given for her armament both before and during her oceanographic voyage. The plans show that the main deck was provided with 22 gun ports and that during the refit all of the guns were removed with the exception of two, presumably the muzzle-loading 68 pounders.

Credit for the instigation of the *Challenger* Expedition must go mainly to W.B. Carpenter who had become convinced, as early as 1869, that the British Government should finance a major scientific circumnavigation. After the successful voyages in the *Lightning* in 1868 and the *Porcupine* in 1869 and 1870 Carpenter, himself a Vice-President of the Royal Society, wrote to the Society's Secretary, G.G. Stokes, suggesting that a plan for marine research should be drawn up jointly with other scientific bodies and submitted to Parliament. The Society accordingly set up a committee including Carpenter, Wyville Thomson, Gwyn Jeffreys, T.H. Huxley, Sir William Thomson, J.D. Hooker and the Hydrographer, G.H. Richards. On the recommendation of this committee the Society's Council asked the government to send out a scientific expedition and the application received approval in April 1872, only nine months before the vessel eventually set sail.

Burstyn (1968) pointed out that a number of factors contributed to the success of the application, including the support of Richards at a time when the Hydrographic Department was being forced into the deep ocean by the needs of submarine telegraphy, the fear that Britain's lead in deep sea science would be eclipsed by other countries, and particularly by the United States, and even the fact that the government's financial structure had recently been reformed under Gladstone's Chancellorship. But is is clear that Carpenter's personal acquaintance with senior ministers, including Gladstone himself, was of crucial importance.

Up to this time the *Challenger* had had a fairly undistinguished career, having served first on the coasts of North America and in the West Indies and, from 1866, on the Australian station. She had returned to England in March 1871 and was still in commission but not in use. Having been selected for the oceanographic expedition she was rapidly refitted at Sheerness, having laboratories and accommodation installed for the scientists and their equipment and an 18 horse power steam donkey engine to haul the trawls and dredges. One of the main modifications was the installation of a dredging platform over the upper deck forward of the main mast from which the dredges and trawls could be deployed and recovered and the refuse from the samples could be thrown overboard without dirtying the Navy's precious deck!

Command of the vessel was given to G.S. Nares who had returned recently from the Mediterranean and Red Sea where he had been in command of the *Shearwater*. Second in command was J.L.P. Maclear, while the lieutenants were Pelham Aldrich and A.C.B. Bromley, together with T.H. Tizard and G.R. Bethel, both of whom had been with Nares in the *Shearwater*.

The civilian scientists appointed by the Royal Society were led by Charles Wyville Thomson, by then Professor of Natural History in the University of Edinburgh, since Carpenter, already 59 years old, had decided not to go to sea again. Thomson was assisted by three naturalists, the most important in retrospect being John Murray who eventually took over responsibility for seeing the Expedition's Scientific Reports through the press after Thomson's death and became the leading figure in British oceanography well into the present century. When the Expedition was being planned, however, Murray was junior to H.N. Moseley, who wrote the most readable scientific account of the voyage, and to William Stirling who resigned his appointment before the voyage began and was replaced by the German biologist Rudolf von Willemöes-Suhm who had visited Thomson in Edinburgh during the German North Sea

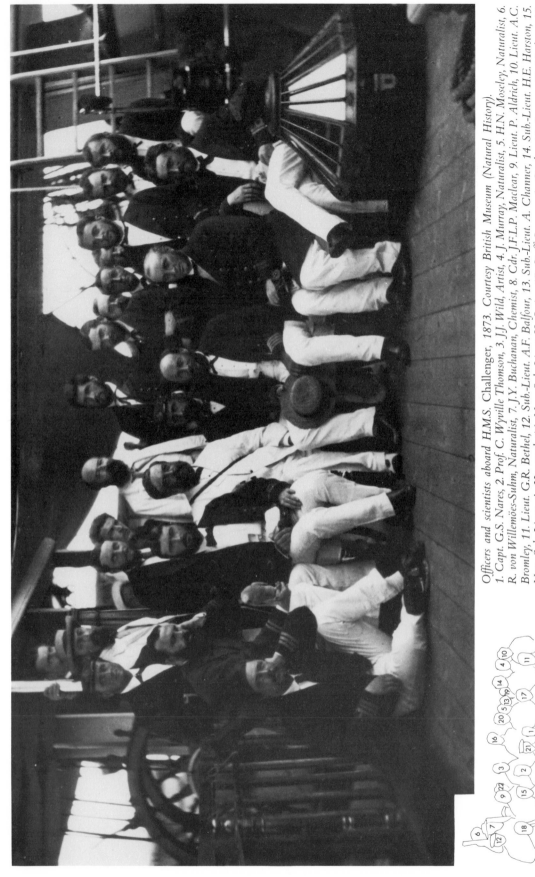

Officers and scientists aboard H.M.S. Challenger, 1873. Courtesy British Museum (Natural History).
1. Capt. G.S. Nares, 2. Prof. C. Wyville Thomson, 3. J.J. Wild, Artist, 4. J. Murray, Naturalist, 5. H.N. Moseley, Naturalist, 6. R. von Willemöes-Suhm, Naturalist, 7. J.Y. Buchanan, Chemist, 8. Cdr. J.F.L.P. Maclear, 9. Lieut. P. Aldrich, 10. Lieut. A.C. Bromley, 11. Lieut. G.R. Bethel, 12. Sub.-Lieut. A.F. Balfour, 13. Sub.-Lieut. A. Channer, 14. Sub.-Lieut. H.E. Harston, 15. Nav. Sub.-Lieut. A. Havergal, 16. Nav. Sub.-Lieut. H. Swire, 17. Staff Surgeon A. Crosby, 18. Surgeon G. Maclean, 19. Paymaster R.R.A. Richards, 20. Ass. Paymaster J. Hynes, 21. Engineer W.J.J. Spry, 22. Ass. Engineer W.A. Houlett. The dog is probably "Boss", belonging to Channer, which was lost in a penguin colony on Nightingale Island.

Expedition in 1871. Willemöes-Suhm was a talented scientist whose promising career was cut short tragically when he died of erysipelas when the ship was in the Pacific, one of only seven deaths amongst the ship's complement, a good record for the time. The scientific team was completed by J.Y. Buchanan who sailed as chemist, while the international flavour was augmented by the Swiss J. J. Wild who acted as artist and Secretary to Thomson. For the duration of the voyage Thomson received an annual salary of £1,000 in compensation for his professorship which he had temporarily resigned, while the naturalists each received £200 a year. Wild received £400 a year apparently because, in contrast with the younger naturalists, he was "a gentleman of middle age and high attainments."

The ship sailed from Portsmouth on 21 December 1872 and called at Lisbon, Gibraltar and Madeira before arriving at Tenerife on 7 February 1873. Although soundings, temperature measurements and dredge samples were obtained during this early part of the cruise, it was treated as a "shake-down" period and the first official station was worked on 15 February in a depth of 1890 fathoms (3560m), some 40 miles south of Tenerife.

During the remainder of 1873 the *Challenger* criss-crossed the Atlantic making many landfalls including stops at St Thomas in the Virgin Islands, Bermuda, Halifax, the Azores, the Cape Verdes, St Paul's Rocks, Bahia, Tristan da Cunha and Cape Town where the ship was refitted and a deck house was built for the naturalists. During the seven week stay in South Africa the most important zoological discovery had nothing to do with oceanography, for Moseley became the first qualified naturalist to examine fresh specimens of the enigmatic little caterpillar-like animal *Peripatus,* demonstrating that it is a primitive arthropod rather than a worm as was thought previously.

After leaving Simon's Bay on 17 December, the *Challenger* sailed into the southern Indian Ocean calling at Marion Island and reaching the Crozet Islands on New Year's Eve. Early in 1874 she called at Kerguelen and Heard Islands before heading south to encounter her first iceberg on 11 February and the edge of the pack ice on 14th. Since there was no intention to reach a particularly high latitude, no attempt was made to enter the pack. Instead, the expedition's furthest south station was worked at about 65°S and the ship then headed more or less eastward, along the edge of the pack. For two weeks *Challenger* was rarely out of sight of icebergs, 88 being within sight early on 24 February. Later that same day the vessel experienced the most dangerous few hours of the whole voyage when she collided with one iceberg during a gale and was almost run down by a second.

By March 1 the ship was almost clear of the ice and sail was set for Melbourne, arriving 16 days later having spent three months almost continuously at sea. Having come from South Africa almost exclusively in high latitudes the expedition had entirely missed the Indian Ocean, apparently partly because it was expected that the Royal Indian Marine Survey would cover this region. This was not to be so (see under *Investigator*) and more than half a century was to pass before systematic studies of the area were made, first from the *Dana* and then from the *Mabahiss.*

After two weeks at Melbourne, refitting and provisioning, the ship sailed to Sydney where her steam pinnace was used for extensive dredging in the harbour during the two-month stay.

From Sydney the *Challenger* had a stormy passage to Wellington where she stayed for only a few days before sailing on to the Kermadecs, Tonga, Fiji, the New Hebrides and Cape York on Australia's far northern shore. From here she followed a tortuous route through the enclosed seas and channels between the islands of the East Indies, calling at the Aru Islands, Amboina and the Philippines before arriving at Hong Kong where she remained from November 17, 1874 to January 6, 1875.

At Hong Kong, Nares left to take command of the British Arctic Expedition in the *Alert,* taking Pelham Aldrich with him; they were replaced by Capt. F.T. Thomson and Lieut. A. Carpenter.

Relics of the Challenger *Ball given for the citizens of Cape Town in December, 1876.*

During their many port calls the Challenger *naturalists and some of the officers continued their scientific pursuits, making important biological and ethnological collections, many of which were reported on along with the oceanographic results. However, they also had a full social life, playing cricket, shooting, fishing, sight-seeing and being entertained by the locals. The* Challenger's *return entertainment was sometimes quite lavish. The Cape Town Ball, for instance, had this specially designed programme and, according to Sub.-Lieut. Arthur Channer's journal, a centre-piece of "the Abyssinian gun drooped round with the Jack and ensign with rifles piled round[;] under[neath] was the dredge and water bottle". Channer, a talented artist, was amused by the sight of the rear view of his fellow Sub.-Lieut., W.J.J. Spry, escorting two ladies of dramatically differing build. His sketch is reproduced with the kind permission of Mr. J.A.J. Murray.*

After the expedition, Channer was seconded to the Royal Indian Marine Survey and eventually became Superintendent of the Ceylon and Minicoy Imperial Light Service.

After leaving Hong Kong the ship more or less retraced her course to the Philippines, before sailing on to New Guinea and then northwards, via the Admiralty Islands to Yokohama. It was during this northerly leg, between the Caroline and Marianas Islands in what became known as the Marianas Trench, that the deepest sounding of the voyage was obtained at a depth of 4475 fathoms (8150m).

Challenger left Japan on 16 June 1875 after a two-month stay during which the social highlight was an impressive, but austere, audience with the Emperor Mutsuhito.

The ship's course now described a great Z through the Pacific, first due east then south via Honolulu and Hilo in the Sandwich Islands to Tahiti, Willemöes-Suhm becoming ill and dying on the way. Finally, she sailed east once more to Juan Fernandez and Valparaiso, arriving on 19 November, 1875.

Early in 1876 the *Challenger* passed through the Straits of Magellan into the Atlantic. After visiting the Falklands and Montevideo she followed a sinuous route through the middle of the Atlantic, via Ascension and the Cape Verdes, making observations which largely complemented those made over the quite different outward route three years before. After a coaling stop at Vigo the *Challenger* returned home to anchor off Spithead on 24 May 1876 having been away for 1281 days, of which 713 had been spent at sea covering 68,890 nautical miles.

By modern standards the voyage had been a rather leisurely affair, the vessel occupying some 362 official stations more or less uniformly distributed along the track so that in general a station would be worked every two or three days. The passages between stations were made almost entirely under sail, conserving the precious coal for station work when it was essential to maintain the ship's position against wind and sea, particularly for obtaining accurate soundings. For towing nets across the sea-floor, however, neither sails nor engines were used, the ship simply being allowed to drift beam on to the sea.

At most of the stations a sounding and a sample of the bottom sediment was taken using hemp lines and initially a *Hydra* sounding tube, replaced from 1873 by the modification of this sounder designed by Lieut. C.W. Baillie. The ship had also been provided with Sir William Thomson's machine for sounding with pianowire, tested successfully from the *Lalla Rookh* in June 1872, but the drum collapsed during its first use on the *Challenger* and it was never tried again. The reliance on rope rather than wire, both for sounding and for towing nets, has been cited as symbolic of a certain conservatism in the *Challenger* Expedition which extended to many other areas. Certainly, by the time she reached the Pacific in 1875 she was already behind the times, for Capt. George Belknap of the U.S.S. *Tuscarora* had produced an improved version of Thomson's machine and had obtained successful soundings using wire along a proposed cable route across the North Pacific during the previous year.

Meanwhile, on the *Challenger* the water temperature was taken at the surface and at the bottom at each station, and frequently at a number of intermediate levels. These deep-sea temperature measurements, in Tizard's charge, were mainly made using Miller-Casella thermometers based on the Six maximum-minimum instrument as used on the *Porcupine*. In 1874 the ship was supplied with Negretti and Zambra's new reversing thermometers which recorded only a single temperature, at the depth where the thermometer was reversed, rather than the extremes to which the instrument had been exposed in the water column. The new thermometers could also be read to a much greater accuracy than the Miller-Casella instruments and eventually took over from them. During the *Challenger* voyage, however, although several series of measurements were taken to compare the performance of the two thermometers, the old Miller-Casella ones continued to be used for the bulk of the determinations. Lieut. Bethel also conducted tests with a modified version of the Siemens electrical resistance thermometer which had been unsuccessfully used in the *Porcupine* in 1869. These *Challenger* tests were quite successful, the results from the resistance thermometers agreeing with those from the other instruments. However, the equipment was still quite difficult to use at sea and Nares had it sent back to England when they reached South Africa late in 1873. It would have been extremely valuable only a few weeks later when a temperature inversion was encountered in the water column at high latitudes in the Southern Ocean, but the detailed temperature structure of the deeper layers could not be determined by the maximum-minimum thermometers with which they were left.

Near-bottom water samples were collected with a 'slip' water bottle, made of brass, in which a cylinder suspended on a central core was released when the bottle struck the sea-bed and slid down the core onto machined surfaces to enclose the water sample. Samples from mid-water were obtained with water bottles designed by Buchanan in which stop-cocks at either end of the bottle were closed by a system of levers operated by the water pressure on a hinged plate as the bottle was hauled through the water column.

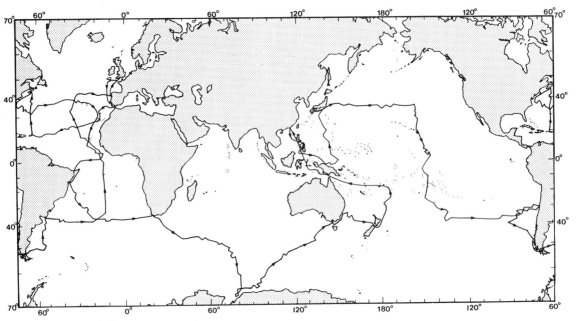

Track of H.M.S. Challenger *1872-1876.*

Finally, biological samples were collected from mid-water and from the sea-floor. The mid-water samples were obtained with open tow-nets, generally towed horizontally at a depth of about 50 fathoms (90m) but occasionally to as deep as 800 fathoms (1460m); sometimes these nets were towed vertically on ropes lowered to 3000m or more. Sea-floor samples were obtained either with iron-framed dredges, up to 5 feet across or, more often, with beam trawls with wooden beams ranging in length from 17 feet for the shallower stations to ten feet for the deepest ones. The use of such trawls in deep water was something of a risk since, whereas the dredges would fish equally well either way up, the trawls would not, and it was impossible to know whether they had worked effectively until they were retrieved. Alexander Agassiz and Capt. Charles D. Sigsbee were to overcome this problem during the cruises of the U.S. Coast-Survey steamer *Blake* in 1877-78 by developing what became known as the Agassiz trawl which, like the earlier dredges, would fish either way up.

The speed and direction of the surface currents were recorded fairly routinely, while from time to time the subsurface currents were also measured using current drogues similar to those which Nares and Carpenter had used from the *Shearwater*.

Most of the results of the Expedition had to await the subsequent land-based examination of the data and samples collected, but a number of important discoveries were made during the voyage itself. Some of these discoveries answered questions which the scientists had sailed with, others were totally unexpected.

By March 1873 the *Porcupine* dredging results, suggesting that life existed at all depths in the ocean, seemed to be confirmed for they had dredged animals from a depth of almost 3000 fathoms (5400m). Since they had already crossed the central parts of the Atlantic without finding much deeper water it seemed probable that significantly greater depths did not exist. Subsequently they encountered considerably deeper water in the Atlantic, obtaining a sounding of 3875 fathoms (7050m) in the Puerto Rico Trench, and much greater depths in the Pacific. No biological samples were obtained at these depths, but the dredges or trawls were used successfully on 25 occasions in water more than 2500 fathoms (c. 4500m) deep, the deepest being at a depth of 3125 fathoms (5700m) on the edge of the Japan Trench in the western Pacific. Since a wide variety of animal life was found in all of these samples, the premature conclusion that life existed throughout the oceans seemed to be amply confirmed.

The sediment samples revealed that the deep sea floor was not universally covered with calcareous muds made up largely of the foraminiferan skeletons, as they had expected. Instead, in the deeper areas the chalky deposits were replaced by red clays of volcanic origin or, particularly in the Pacific, siliceous sediments formed largely from radiolarian remains. Moreover, the townet samples clearly demonstrated that many of the organisms whose skeletons made up these deposits lived in the surface waters and were not bottom dwellers as Wyville Thomson and Carpenter believed. Another unexpected feature of the sea-floor samples was the presence of manganese nodules, often with a shark's tooth as a nucleus, which were first encountered during the passage through the Atlantic but which were found to be individually larger and much more numerous in the Pacific.

Murray's townetting results also provided new evidence for the diurnal vertical migration of mid-water animals, though the phenomenon had first been observed during Bellingshausen's Antarctic voyage of 1819 to 1821. In the absence of opening and closing nets capable of taking samples from discrete depth horizons, Murray could detect the migration only by comparing day and night catches at the surface.

During the early part of the voyage the sediment samples were examined assiduously for evidence of the primitive life form, *Bathybius,* which T.H. Huxley had described from mud samples collected from the *Cyclops* in 1858 and which subsequently had been recorded by a number of expeditions, including those of the *Lightning* and *Porcupine.* For more than two and a half years no sign of *Bathybius* was found, and then it was noticed that the sediment samples preserved in spirit contained a jelly-like substance which corresponded to Huxley's description but that this material was not present in the samples preserved in water. Buchanan demonstrated that the mysterious substance had resulted from the precipitation of calcium sulphate from the sea water in the samples by the alcohol used for preservation. Thomson's letter to Huxley informing him of this discovery led to Huxley's frank published admission that he had been mistaken.

Carpenter had hoped that the subsurface temperature and specific gravity determinations made during the voyage would provide incontrovertible evidence in support of the theory of general oceanic circulation to which he subscribed. According to this theory the major water movements in the deep oceans were due to differences in the density of the water masses caused by the heating and cooling effects at the equator and at the poles, rather than being driven by the winds. Carpenter's views were subsequently largely substantiated, but his hopes for the voyage were not to be realised, for there was no-one directly associated with the venture with sufficient knowledge of physics to unravel what was a much more complex situation than he thought. As a consequence, the physical results were generally rather disappointing compared with the biological ones alongside which they were intended originally to rank equally. Nevertheless, the deep temperature measurements made in the Atlantic during both the outward passage in 1873 and the homeward journey in 1876 led to startling suggestions about the morphology of the deep sea floor. Differences in the bottom temperatures recorded in the various basins enabled the *Challenger* personnel to forecast the existence of a continuous mid-Atlantic and subsidiary ridge system long before these features were detectable from the available soundings, though the *Challenger* soundings did indicate a continuous ridge between Tristan da Cunha and Ascension.

Preliminary accounts of most of these discoveries were published before the ship returned, mainly in the journal *Nature,* while numerous relatively short papers on the biological collections appeared in a variety of scientific journals, particularly the *Annals and Magazine of Natural History* and the journals of the Linnean and Zoological Societies of London. Curiously, the first attempt at a synthesis of the physical results was made not by the scientists but by the secretary / artist Wild (1877). However, the bulk of the Expedition results appeared in the official Scientific Reports published in 50 volumes, containing a total of almost 30,000 pages, between 1880 and 1895. The task of editing these reports fell first to Thomson and then, after his death in 1882, to Murray. Thomson established the Challenger Office in Edinburgh and from here the marine collections were sent out to specialists in Europe and North America as well as in the United Kingdom, with the intention that the material should be studied by the most able scientists available and should be deposited in the Natural History collections of the British Museum once they had been worked up. This plan received considerable opposition at home since the Museum authorities maintained that the collections should be deposited in London immediately, while many British scientists felt that the opportunity to work on the material should go first to their own number. After some difficulty Thomson got his own way and, as a direct result, Edinburgh was for some years the centre for the marine sciences and the emerging discipline of oceanography gained the international flavour which it still has.

These controversies, and also the problems which Thomson and Murray experienced in dealing with the Treasury and the Stationery Office over the publication of the Reports, have been dealt with adequately by Deacon (1971) and Burstyn (1968). The difficulties with the official Departments resulted largely from the British Government's reluctance to pour more money into what was already considered to have been an extremely expensive exercise. Having suffered, and overcome, the parsimony of the Treasury and completed the publication of the Reports, John Murray claimed in 1913 that the Government had by that time received more than the cost of the Expedition in revenues from the Christmas Island Phosphate Company which he had been instrumental in forming as a direct result of his interest in coral formations which had begun during the voyage. Burstyn (1975) carefully examined the sums involved and estimated the total cost of the venture as about £170,000, concluding that while Murray's 1913 claim was a "pardonable exaggeration" it would certainly have been true by 1921 at the latest.

Not all of the problems were financial, however, a totally unforeseen one resulting in the following note being attached to one of the volumes of the Report:

"This is one of the copies referred to in the following Extract from the Third Report of the Controller of Her Majesty's Stationery Office, presented to Parliament in 1890:-

The publication of the reports, by no means all of which, as your Lordships will recollect, were prepared in Great Britain or Ireland, has gone on without any mishap until a few months ago, when, unfortunately, a steamer carrying from Leith to London 306 copies of a volume then lately issued, was run into and sunk off the Lincolnshire coast. Among the damaged cargo afterwards recovered from the wreck and sold by auction by direction of the honourable Corporation of Trinity House, under the Removal of Wrecks Acts, 1877, were 13 cases containing about 190 of the lost "Challenger" volumes, in a more or less spongy state. These were brought back to the Stationery Office. They have since been taken out of the covers and dried, and it seems probable that from them, with the addition of new copies of some of the plates which happen still to remain on the stone, about 100 copies may be made up, stained, but for all practical purposes perfect. The copies thus made up will not, unless specifically asked for, be issued for sale until the uninjured stock of the volume is exhausted. It is not impossible that in the eyes of future owners the imperfections of the recovered volumes may be compensated for by the knowledge that the book, like the "Alcyonaria" and "Polyzoa", which are beautifully figured in them, have been drawn from the bottom of the sea."

When Hedgpeth referred to these recovered copies in 1946 he said that their pages still tasted of salt. When I recently tested the relevant Institute of Oceanographic Sciences copy, out of the sight of librarians, I could taste nothing!

After her brief foray into the oceanographic limelight the active career of the *Challenger* was almost at an end. She was commissioned as a Coast Guard and Drill Ship of Naval Reserves at Harwich in July 1876, and was finally paid off at Chatham in 1878. In 1880 she was converted into a receiving hulk and remained in this capacity in the river at Chatham until 1921 when she was broken up.

References:

The following list does not pretend to be exhaustive, but it contains all of those accounts of the voyage which were produced by the participants and also most of the spate of *Challenger* references which appeared around the centenary of the Expedition.

Burstyn, 1968, 1972, 1975; Campbell, 1877; Charnock, 1973; Deacon, 1971; Deacon M.B. and Deacon G.E.R., 1972; Hedgpeth, 1946; Linklater, 1972; McConnell, 1982; Merriman, 1972; Mills, 1972, 1973a, b; Rice, 1972, 1983; Spry, 1895; Stoddart, 1972; Swire, 1938; Thomson, C.W. 1877; Wild, 1877, 1878; Willemöes-Suhm, 1877; Yonge, 1972a, b.

HMS CHALLENGER

Survey vessel, built Chatham Dockyard 1931, 1140 tons gross, 200' long, 36' beam, 1200 i.h.p.

The *Challenger* was originally intended for surveying new fishing grounds in northern waters and was to have been paid for by the Ministry of Agriculture and Fisheries but administered and run by the Hydrographic Department of the Admiralty. However, in the difficult financial situation in 1931 the Ministry was unable to afford the vessel and she was eventually taken over by the Admiralty as a survey vessel to replace the *Iroquois* which was then about to end her surveying career.

From 1932 to the outbreak of the Second World War the *Challenger* was employed under a succession of commanders in surveying off the coast of Labrador, in the West Indies and in the Persian Gulf. During her various passages through the Atlantic in this period she worked many hydrographic stations, obtaining data on the vertical distribution of temperature and salinity which were incorporated in the echo-sounding correction tables prepared by D.J. Matthews to make allowance for the effects of variations in the physical characteristics of the water column on the speed of sound passing through it.

During the early part of the war the vessel was engaged in vital surveys of anchorages, channels and boom defences in British and Icelandic waters and also carried out a survey of the Gambia River in 1941-42. From 1942 to the end of hostilities *Challenger* served with the Eastern fleet in the Indian Ocean and south western Pacific, actually printing charts resulting from her surveys on the spot. After the war she was used for routine surveys in the Persian Gulf and around the coast of Cyprus, returning to Chatham in 1949. Here she was refitted for her last major cruise and her most significant contribution to the development of oceanography.

H.M.S. Challenger, *photographed 1946. Reproduced by permission of the Hydrographer to the Navy.*

Since the end of the war there had been an increasing interest in the shape of the deep ocean basins and the nature of the sea floor. The Swedish training vessel *Albatross* had already completed a circumnavigation in 1947-48 carrying out sea-floor coring work, while the Danish vessel *Galathea* was about to begin a two year voyage which was to be principally biological, but which would also echo-sound across the main ocean basins. The Hydrographer, Sir Guy Wyatt, therefore determined to send the *Challenger* on a similar world survey to carry out extensive echo-sounding in deep water.

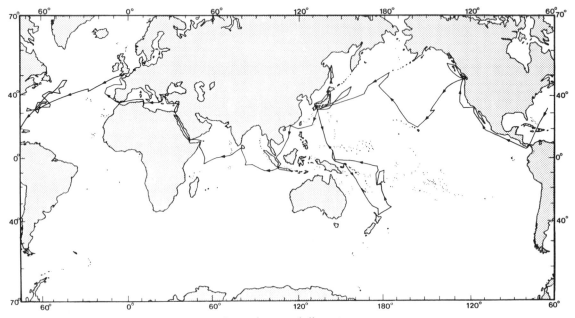

Track of H.M.S. Challenger *in 1950-52. Redrawn from Gaskell, 1960.*

At the same time, Dr. Maurice Hill of the Department of Geodesy and Geophysics in Cambridge had recently devised a technique by which seismic reflection work, originally developed by the American geophysicist Maurice Ewing, could be carried out from a single vessel using free-floating sono-buoys to determine the nature and thickness of sub-seafloor strata. The combination of deep sounding and seismic reflection was ideal and two Cambridge scientists, T.F. Gaskell and J.C. Swallow, accompanied the *Challenger* to carry out the seismic work.

Between 1950 and 1952 the ship travelled over 75,000 miles through the Atlantic, Pacific and Indian Oceans and the Red Sea and Mediterranean, initially under Cdr. R. Bill and subsequently under Cdr. G.S. Ritchie after Bill was taken ill and had to leave the ship in Bermuda.

A number of seismic refraction stations were carried out in each of the major oceans and seismic reflection work was conducted more or less routinely each day, these being the first studies by this technique in the Mediterranean. Echo-soundings were made as a routine throughout the cruise, including a survey of the *Challenger* Deep in the Marianas Trench where the deepest sounding recorded to that time, 5900 fathoms (10791m), was obtained with the taut wire apparatus usually used for surveying. A bottom sample was obtained with a Baillie Rod from a depth of 5774 fathoms (10560m). In 1957 the Russian oceanographic vessel *Vityaz* confirmed the *Challenger's* sounding with an echo-sounder and in 1960 the bathyscaphe *Trieste* reached the bottom of the trench and determined the depth as 6300 fathoms (11523m) by pressure measurements.

There was no biologist aboard the *Challenger,* but the ship's doctor had been given a short course in marine biology at the Marine Biological Association Laboratory in Plymouth before the vessel sailed. Surface plankton hauls were routinely taken each morning, but the samples do not seem to have been worked up.

After the *Challenger* returned from the world voyage she made a series of short seismic and sounding cruises in the north Atlantic, paying off for the last time in Plymouth in September 1953 and being broken up in 1954.

References:
Gaskell, 1960; Ritchie, 1957.

HMS CHANTICLEER

"Cherokee" class brig-sloop (cf. *Beagle*), built Cowes 1808, 237 (bm) c. 90' long, 25' beam.
Under the command of Capt. Henry Foster the *Chanticleer* cruised in the South Atlantic and around the South Shetlands in 1828-31. Foster used Marcet's water bottles and Six thermometers and carried out pendulum and magnetic observations at Deception Island.

Foster was drowned in the Chagres River in 1831 when he fell from a canoe returning to the *Chanticleer.*

The *Chanticleer* became a Customs watch vessel on her return to England and was designated WV5 in 1863 (cf. *Beagle*). *Chanticleer* was broken up at Sheerness in 1871.

References:
Deacon, 1971; Jones, 1974; McConnell, 1984; Webster, 1834.

RIMS CLYDE

Indian naval wooden screw gunboat, built Bombay Dockyard 1859, 300 (bm), 125' long, 23' beam.

When the Royal Indian Marine Survey was established in 1874 the *Clyde* was assigned to it and was used for shallow-water dredging, to depths of about 100 fathoms (182m), by the Survey's first Surgeon-Naturalist, J. Armstrong, who occupied the post from 1875 to 1879.

Reference:

Alcock, 1898.

HMS CONGO

Paddle survey schooner, 1-12 pdr, built Deptford 1816, 83 (bm), 70′ long, 16′ beam.

The *Congo* was built specifically for an expedition to sail up the River Congo to investigate the theory that it was in some way connected with the Niger, the upper reaches of which had been explored by Mungo Park in 1795. This was the first Naval expedition despatched by John Barrow, Second Secretary to the Admiralty, after the end of the Napoleonic wars left large numbers of ships and officers unemployed. Command of the expedition was given to Captain James Kingston Tuckey who had carried out the first survey of Sydney harbour and had written a major work on maritime geography while held captive by the French at Verdun.

Tuckey took the *Dorothea* as a transport, sending her back from the mouth of the Congo. The expedition was disastrous, and by the time the *Congo* had reached 200 miles up the river all of the officers, including Tuckey, were dead, as were most of the crew.

A few marine biological samples had been obtained, mainly in the immediate vicinity of the mouth of the Congo, but the scientific results cannot be considered as significant in the development of oceanography. Instead, the expedition deserves a place in the history of marine science for two curiously negative reasons. First, if the venture had not been such an unmitigated disaster it is likely that Barrow would have concentrated more of the Royal Navy's efforts in the post-Napoleonic war period into African exploration. Instead, Barrow turned the navy's attentions to the Arctic, beginning with the voyages of the *Isabella, Alexander, Dorothea* and *Trent* in 1818 and followed by the long series of expeditions to high latitudes which continued throughout most of the nineteenth century and which resulted in the accumulation of so much oceanographic data. Second, the *Congo* was originally intended to be a paddle steamer, with a 20 h.p. engine supplied by the Tyneside engineers Boulton and Watt to drive her against the current in the Congo. Had this intention been realised, the *Congo* would have held an important place in the history of navigation as the first powered vessel in the Royal Navy. In the event, however, a misunderstanding between the engineers and the naval architects resulted in a vessel which was too narrow and therefore had too great a draught to take the 30 ton engine in safety. Barrow therefore had the engine removed and the *Congo* was rigged as a schooner. During the next few years several naval steam tugs were introduced, beginning with the *Monkey* (1819) and the *Comet* (1822), but it was not until 1828, that the Navy List contained the first powered warships, including the *Lightning* (launched 1823) which made her own very important contribution to oceanography forty years later.

References:

Lloyd, 1970; Tuckey, 1816 (inc. Barrow's introduction).

HMS CYCLOPS

"Cyclops" class paddle frigate, 2-98 pdr, 4-68 pdr, built Pembroke Dock 1839, 1195 (bm), 190′3″ long, 37′ beam, 320 n.h.p. The *Cyclops* was the second paddle frigate built for the

Royal Navy and was to have been similar to the *Gorgon,* the first of this type. However, both vessels were fitted with larger engines than had been intended originally and the length of the *Cyclops* was increased by twelve feet to give her a greater coal capacity.

Under the command of Lieut. Joseph Dayman, who had been Owen Stanley's First Lieutenant on the *Rattlesnake,* the *Cyclops* carried out the first British sounding survey for the North Atlantic submarine telegraph cable in 1857. The vessel had been fitted as a tug at Sheerness in 1851 and was refitted for the sounding voyage at a cost of £13,184.

Interest in deep-sea soundings was greatly stimulated in the 1850s and 1860s by developments in submarine telegraphy. Plans for a transatlantic cable began to be made shortly after the first successful cross Channel cable was laid in 1851 and good bathymetric surveys of suitable routes became a high priority for both the British and American navies.

H.M.S. Cyclops *off Spithead. Artist W. Knell. Courtesy National Maritime Museum. Neg. no. X 628.*

The use in deep water of the relatively heavy line used for conventional shallow water soundings was not successful, for the weight of the line and its resistance in the water made detection of the arrival of the weight on the sea-bed very difficult. In 1850, Matthew Fontaine Maury, Director of the National Observatory in Washington, had introduced the use of very light line and a relatively heavy weight in which the rate of descent of the weight was timed and its arrival on the bottom was determined by this rate markedly slowing. Maury's technique proved to be less successful than was initially hoped and many clearly erroneous soundings were reported with its use. In any case, the line was not sufficiently strong to retrieve the weight, or a sample of the sea-floor sediment. Since it was essential to know the nature of the sea-floor, this difficulty had to be overcome by releasing part of the sounding weight when it reached the bottom, thus reducing the load to be retrieved. In 1852, John Brooke, a young midshipman in the U.S. Navy, devised a system in which a rod armed with tallow at its lower end to collect a sediment sample passed through a spherical weight which was supported by a cord sling hooked onto a detaching mechanism at the top of the rod. When the instrument reached the sea-floor and weight came off the sounding line, the sling was released.   When the line was hauled, the weight slid off the rod which returned to the surface with its mud sample.   Brooke's sounder became widely used in both the American and British navies but was modified by almost every officer who used it.

In 1856 a version with a tapered sinker and with a valve on the sampler tube to prevent loss of the sediment was used by Lieut. Otway Berryman for a survey of a cable route from Newfoundland to Ireland in the U.S.S. *Arctic.* Maury rejected the resulting profile of the Atlantic because Berryman's results during the east-west voyage did not agree with those obtained in the opposite direction, and it was clear that insufficient care had been taken with the soundings and the navigation.   Dayman's cruise on the *Cyclops* was therefore intended to repeat and improve Berryman's survey over a slightly more northerly course.

Dayman used a modified Brooke sounder in which the sinker was elongated rather than spherical, iron stays replaced the cord sling and, as in Berryman's sounder, the sediment sampling tube was fitted with a valve.

In June and July 1857 he obtained a total of 34 deep soundings and sediment samples down to 2400 fathoms (4300m) on a route from Valencia in Southern Ireland to Newfoundland.   In 1858 and 1859 Dayman carried out further sounding surveys in the *Gorgon* and *Firebrand,* becoming by far the most experienced sounding officer in the British navy.   He was nevertheless passed over in favour of Sir Leopold M'Clintock for the command of the *Bulldog* for the survey of a more northerly cable route in 1860.

In addition to the sounding results, the *Cyclops* voyage has a rather notorious place in the history of oceanography because of the controversy arising from the sediment samples which were sent to Thomas Henry Huxley, palaeontologist at the London School of Mines.   Huxley found them to contain many dead foraminiferan shells, like previously described deep-sea samples, and he wrote a short report on them which was published with Dayman's account of the sounding results.   Ten years later, however, he re-examined the samples and announced to the world the presence in them of a gelatinous, mucus-like material, with a variety of calcareous inclusions, including coccoliths.   Huxley identified the material as the protoplasm of the simplest organism so far discovered and which he christened *Bathybius haeckelii.*

The discovery of *Bathybius* was widely welcomed by many scientists who had embraced Darwin's recently published explanation of evolution, and particularly by the German biologist Ernst Haeckel after whom it was named and who saw the new "organism" as representing living protoplasm being spontaneously generated on the ocean floor from inorganic materials.   Further reports of its widespread occurrence were soon forthcoming, from the Atlantic in the dredge hauls of the *Lightning* and *Porcupine* in 1868 and 1869 and from Oscar Schmidt's dredgings in the Adriatic in 1870.   An even simpler form, lacking inclusions, was found in Smith Sound in 1872 during the American North Pole Expedition.

In Wyville Thomson's general account of the *Lightning* and *Porcupine* cruises, *The Depths of the Sea,* published as the *Challenger* sailed, the *Challenger's* scientific leader expressed some doubts about the nature of *Bathybius.*   He was convinced, for instance, that the association of coccoliths with *Bathybius* was purely adventitious, while he suggested that some of the material reported as *Bathybius* was actually organic residue "connected either with the growth and multiplication or with the decay–of many different things."

Nevertheless, *Challenger* scientists eagerly looked for signs of *Bathybius* in all of the sediment samples brought aboard–with no success.   Finally, in the spring of 1875, more than two years into the voyage, the expedition chemist, J.Y. Buchanan, examined some jelly-like material found in sediment samples which John Murray had preserved in alcohol.   Buchanan thought the material had all the essential characteristics of *Bathybius,* but when he analysed it he found that it consisted of calcium sulphate precipitated from the sea water in the samples by the preserving alcohol.   Thomson informed Huxley of Buchanan's findings and the discoverer of *Bathybius* published an admission that he had been mistaken.

Apart from a few attempts to keep the *Bathybius* story alive by some of its more tenacious supporters, including Haeckel, the "organism" was referred to, for over a century, only as an example of how even a brilliant scientist can be badly misled.   In the early 1980s, however, the discovery of the seasonal deposition of phytoplanktonic detritus onto the deep-sea floor prompted the suggestion that this was the source of the material described by Huxley rather than the inorganic chemical explanation offered by Buchanan.

The *Cyclops* was sold in 1864 for £5,000.

References:
Buchanan and Doughty, 1978; Dayman, 1858; Deacon, 1971; Huxley, 1868, 1875; Laing, 1980; McConnell, 1982; Rehbock, 1975; Rice, 1983.

DACIA

Steam screw cable vessel built by J. Laing and Co. at Sunderland 1867, 1856 gross tons, 283' long, 35' beam, 170 h.p.   The vessel was built for Norwood and Company and was purchased by the India-Rubber, Gutta Percha and Telegraph Works Company in 1870 and used during her early years in laying cables in the Caribbean.   From 1883 to 1905 she worked mainly in the Atlantic but also in the Indian Ocean and Arabian Gulf.

Cable ship Dacia. *Courtesy National Maritime Museum. Neg. no. A 2702.*

In 1883 the *Dacia* conducted an unusually detailed sounding survey for a cable ship, accompanied by John Young Buchanan who had been the chemist aboard the *Challenger.* During the previous year the cable ship *Seine,* belonging to the Telegraph Construction and Maintenance Company, had encountered an unsuspected submerged peak, the Seine Bank, between Cadiz and the Canaries, on which the cable had parted.   The *Dacia* was despatched to survey this peak, and any others on the same route which might have been missed by the widely spaced soundings of a conventional survey. By making very closely spaced soundings whenever a slight shoaling of the deep sea bed was encountered, the *Dacia* located the Seine Bank and two other submerged mountains on the proposed route.

The *Dacia* was torpedoed off Funchal in 1916.

References:
Baglehole, 1969; Buchanan 1884-6; Haigh, 1968.

DIANA

Dundee whaler, under the command of Robert Davidson, which accompanied the *Balaena* (q.v.) to the Antarctic in 1892-1893.

HMS DISCOVERY

Wooden screw vessel, 1247 tons displacement, 160' long, 29' beam.

The vessel was originally a whaler named *Bloodhound* and was purchased by the Royal Navy as a storeship in 1874 and renamed to accompany the *Alert* (q.v.) during the British Arctic Expedition under G.S. Nares, the *Discovery* being commanded by H.F. Stephenson.

The *Discovery* was eventually sold in 1902.

H.M.S. Discovery *with H.M.S.* Alert *in the background. From a watercolour "Forcing a passage through the ice", by W.F. Mitchell. Courtesy National Maritime Museum. Neg. no. 9763.*

HMS DISCOVERY

Steam barque built in 1901 by the Dundee Shipbuilders Company to a design by W.E. Smith, an Admiralty Naval architect; length overall 198′, waterline length 172′, 32′ beam, 1620 tons displacement, with two 450 h.p. triple expansion steam engines and lifting propellor and rudder. The vessel was built specially for the National Antarctic Expedition under R.F. Scott who was seconded from the Navy with others of the ship's company. The cost of the ship was £33,700 for the hull excluding the engines.

The expedition was the brain child of Sir Clements Markham, President of the Royal Geographical Society who, for some years, had tried unsuccessfully to encourage the Royal Navy to resume antarctic exploration. Eventually, he decided upon a privately funded expedition with a Naval crew. After some difficulty he raised a total of £45,000 including £10,000 from the R.G.S., and this was ultimately matched by a similar figure from the British Government.

Discovery, *Victoria Harbour, Dundee 1901. Courtesy Dundee Industrial Heritage.*

Discovery sailed from Cowes on 6 August 1901 for Lyttelton, New Zealand, via the Cape. After refitting, the vessel left Lyttelton for the Antarctic on 21 December. Having cleared Cape Adare, Scott sailed down the coast of South Victoria Land to McMurdo Sound and then eastward along the length of the Ice Barrier (now known as the Ross Ice Shelf), discovering King Edward VII Land at its eastern end. The vessel then returned to McMurdo Sound, discovered that Ross Island was, indeed, an island and reached Hut Point, at its southern extremity, where winter quarters were to be established, on 8 February. Here *Discovery* became frozen in and could not be freed the following February when the relief vessel *Morning*, under command of William Colbeck, visited the base. She was eventually freed on 16 February 1904 and left the antarctic in company with the two relief vessels, the *Morning* and *Terra Nova*, reaching Lyttelton on 1 April.

An extensive physical programme was conducted at the winter quarters including tidal, pendulum, seismological, auroral and magnetic observations. The results, incorporating data collected from the *Scotia,* were published by the Royal Society. The oceanographic observations, however, were strictly limited. Surface townets were used relatively routinely during the outward voyage while a small number of deep soundings and dredge hauls were obtained. But most of the marine biological collections, which were deposited in the natural history collections of the British Museum, were taken in the relatively shallow waters of McMurdo Sound under the supervision of the expedition biologist, T.V. Hodgson. The reports on these collections, edited by F. Jeffrey Bell, were published in a series of six volumes which appeared between 1907 and 1912.

After her return from the Antarctic Expedition the ship was purchased in 1905 by the Hudson Bay Company for £10,000 and converted for use in the arctic fur trade. She was employed until 1911 in supplying the Company's posts and bringing back their produce, thereafter being laid up. During the First World War she was chartered by the French Minister of Commerce and for two years carried war materials between England and France using steam power alone, her rigging having been removed. In 1915 she also made a voyage to Archangel carrying munitions.

In 1916 the Hudson Bay Company offered the services of *Discovery* to attempt to rescue the crew of Shackleton's *Endurance,* stranded on Elephant Island in the South Shetlands after the *Endurance* had been crushed and sunk. The ship was refitted by the Admiralty at Devonport, but news of Shackleton's own successful attempt to rescue his men reached the *Discovery* at Montevideo on her way south and accordingly she returned to England. In 1918-19 she made a last voyage to Hudson Bay for the Hudson Bay Company, and in 1919-20 she was chartered by the Merchant Trading Company for a trading voyage to the Russian Black Sea ports of Novorossijsk and Taganrog.

In 1923 she was purchased for £70,000 for what later became known as Discovery Investigations and was extensively renovated and refitted at Vospers in Portsmouth, including the complete provision of new masts, spars, sails and rigging, slightly modified from her original form to improve her sailing properties. With the title of Royal Research Ship (R.R.S.) the vessel was to be employed in scientific investigation of all aspects of the Southern Ocean which had bearing on the antarctic whaling industry, to be financed from a tax levied by the Colonial Government on whale oil passing through the Falkland Islands Dependencies.

The investigations resulted from the recommendations of a report to Parliament by an Interdepartmental Committee which had been set up originally in 1917. After the *Discovery* was purchased, this original committee became known as the Discovery Committee, made up of representatives of the Colonial Office, the Board of Agriculture and Fisheries and the Natural History Museum from the earlier group, together with additional representatives from the Admiralty and the Royal Geographical Society.

It became clear that the work envisaged could not be accomplished by the *Discovery* alone and plans were made for the construction of a second vessel, specially suited for whale marking, eventually resulting in the launch of the *William Scoresby* at the end of 1925.

In 1924 Stanley Kemp, then Superintendent of the Zoological Survey of India, was appointed Director of Research and Leader of the *Discovery* Expedition, and Alister Hardy, an assistant at the Fisheries Laboratory at Lowestoft, became the first member of staff. The planned programme was to fall into two parts, one mainly concerned with the anatomy and embryology of the whales themselves and based at a shore laboratory to be established at the whaling station at Grytviken on South Georgia, the other concerned with observations made at sea.

The shore station was established in the autumn of 1924, that is before *Discovery* sailed, and was staffed by three zoologists, N.A. Mackintosh, J.F.G. Wheeler and L. Harrison Matthews, a hydrologist, A.J. Clowes, and a technician, A. Saunders.

After a false start, in which the *Discovery* suffered storm damage after leaving Porstmouth and had to refit at Dartmouth, the vessel finally sailed from England for South Africa on 24 September 1925. In addition to Kemp and Hardy, the scientific party consisted of J.E. Hamilton, naturalist to the Falkland Islands Government, E.R. Gunther, also a zoologist, and H.F.P. Herdman as hydrologist.

During the passage south, tests were made of the various pieces of equipment to be used routinely in the Southern Ocean, including the newly developed echo-sounder, the results of which were compared with those obtained with a steam driven Lucas sounding machine, and Hardy's prototype continuous plankton recorder. The first official station was worked near Ascension Island on 16 November 1925.

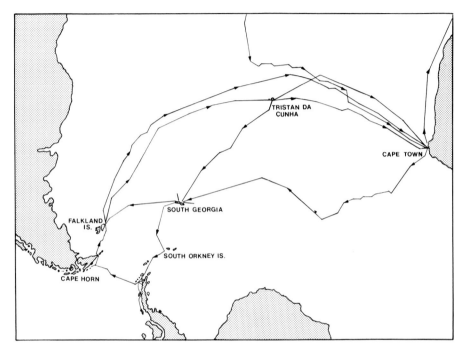

Track of R.R.S. Discovery *during the first part of the* Discovery Investigations *in 1925 to 1927. Redrawn from* Discovery Reports, *Volume 1.*

After spending Christmas at Cape Town the ship sailed on 17 January 1926 for the first of her two cruises to the Scotia Sea region, beginning her "routine" stations after calling at Tristan da Cunha with the island's first delivery of supplies for two and a half years. These routine or standard stations generally involved obtaining a sediment sample with the sounding machine, collecting water samples and temperature measurements using a Nansen-Petterson insulated water bottle to 100m depth and an Ekmann reversing water bottle to 3000m where possible, and taking plankton samples in 50 to 250m depth horizons between the surface and 1000m using vertical closing nets. In addition, dredges were used from time to time to obtain bottom samples, while the echo-sounder and the continuous plankton recorder were used between stations.

On the first cruise the ship worked around South Georgia and then sailed to the Falklands, before returning to Cape Town on 29 June 1926 and later moving to Simonstown where she was joined by the *William Scoresby*. During the cruise the ship's heavy rolling had hindered the use of the scientific gear and bilge keels were therefore fitted at Simonstown in an effort to improve matters.

During the second antarctic cruise, from October 1926 to June 1927, the *Discovery* again worked a series of stations to South Georgia, this time via Bouvetøya (Bouvet Island) and a

R.R.S. Discovery *at Port Lockroy, March 1927. Institute of Oceanographic Sciences. Neg. no. 7019.*

Personnel of the Discovery, William Scoresby *and the Marine Station photographed at Grytviken, South Georgia, on board* Discovery. *Stenhouse (Master of* Discovery*) is seated between Hardy and Kemp, with Mercer (Master of* William Scoresby*) on Kemp's right. Clowes is seated at the extreme right, while standing in civilian clothes are (from the left) Herdman, Fraser, Wheeler, Hamilton, Matthews and Mackintosh. A similar photograph, with more of the personnel identified, is published in Coleman-Cooke, 1963. Photograph Institute of Oceanographic Sciences.*

second series back from the Falklands via Tristan da Cunha. On this cruise, however, after participating with the *Scoresby* in the survey around South Georgia, the *Discovery* worked in the South Shetlands and along the Graham Land peninsula to Port Lockroy before sailing to Port Stanley via Cape Horn and then back to South Africa.

Discovery sailed from Simonstown for England on 18 July and worked a number of stations off south-west Africa and a series to the Cape Verdes, finally arriving at Falmouth on 29 September 1927.

The voyage had been in many ways a great success, the *Discovery* having occupied a total of 299 official stations and having gathered extensive echo-sounding data as well as some 2,300 miles of plankton records with Hardy's recorder. However, it had become clear that the vessel was far from ideal for the work she was expected to carry out. Her accommodation for the scientists and their equipment was inadequate, her fuel capacity was too small for the extensive steaming and station keeping which was demanded of her, the standing rigging hindered the operation of the gear, her engines were old and she was extremely uncomfortable. Consequently, the Discovery Committee decided to replace her with a modern steel ship, *Discovery II,* which eventually sailed on her own first commission in December 1929.

From 1929 to 1931 *Discovery* was used for the British, Australian and New Zealand Antarctic Research Expedition (B.A.N.Z.A.R.E.) under the overall leadership of Sir Douglas Mawson.

The Expedition was partly prompted by scientific and geographical objectives. However, it was also politically motivated by the need to annex what became the Australian Antarctic Territory, recognised at the Imperial Conference in London in 1926 in view of the territorial advances in Antarctica being made by other nations in the 1920s and particularly by the Norwegians.

When Mawson first enquired about the possibility of using the *Discovery* this seemed unlikely since the vessel was expected to be occupied with the Discovery Investigations for some years to come. In the event, the unsuitability of the ship for the scientific work, outlined above, together with the political advantage to Britain of the proposed expedition, changed the situation and the *Discovery* was made available to Mawson from early in 1929. Of the total cost of the Expedition, roughly half (about £60,000) was provided by the British, Australian and New Zealand Governments, the British contribution, £11,714, being used for the hire of the vessel, while the remainder was obtained from private sources.

Discovery left London in August 1929 under the command of J.K. Davis, Mawson and most of the scientific staff travelling by steamer from Australia to join her in South Africa. The scientific team consisted of T. Harvey Johnston, W.W. Ingram and H.O. Fletcher (biologists), R.A. Falla (ornithologist), R.G. Simmers (meteorologist), A. Howard (hydrologist) and M.H. Moyes (echo-sounding and cartographer). In addition, the *Discovery* carried a light aeroplane, flown by Ft. Lieut. Stuart Campbell and Air Pilot E. Douglas, to traverse the pack ice and extend the range of observation. Finally, J.W.S. Marr was loaned by the Discovery Committee to supervise the plankton work since Mawson was anxious to carry out scientific observations of a similar quality to those made by the Discovery Investigations.

After leaving Cape Town on 19 October 1929 (now rigged as a barquentine rather than a barque) the ship visited Kerguelen and Heard Islands and cruised along the Antarctic coast from about 45°E to 80°E, discovering Mac Robertson Land and roughly charting the coastline by ship and aircraft, before sailing via Kerguelen to Australia, arriving at Port Adelaide on 1 April 1930. During this voyage the *Discovery* had met up with the Norwegian vessel *Norvegia* near Cape Ann in Enderby Land and Mawson and Hjalmar Riiser-Larsen agreed on 45°E as the boundary between Norwegian and British activities.

During the southern winter *Discovery* moved to Melbourne and preparations were made for a second voyage. Davis resigned his position because relations between himself and Mawson had been very strained during the first voyage. Command for the second voyage was therefore

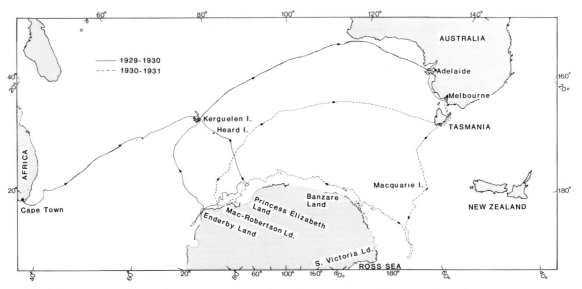

Track of the Discovery *during the B.A.N.Z.A.R. expedition between 1929 and 1931, redrawn from Price, 1963.*

given to K.N. MacKenzie who had previously been the Chief Officer. Marr returned to the Discovery Investigations and Moyes was replaced by A.L. Kennedy, but otherwise the personnel was largely unchanged. *Discovery* left Melbourne in November 1930 and sailed via Tasmania and Macquarie Island to the Antarctic Circle at 180°E. She then sailed westward to Kemp Land, linking up with the previous season's work, discovering the BANZARE Coast and Princess Elizabeth Land in the process and making formal annexing proclamations at five points. The ship finally returned to Hobart on 19 March 1931.

During the two B.A.N.Z.A.R.E. voyages a total of 115 stations were worked, 40 of them being complete hydrographic and plankton stations similar to the standard stations of the Discovery Investigations. In addition, some 20,000 miles of echo-sounding records were obtained and an extensive series of bottom samples were taken with a variety of trawls and dredges. Finally, during the second voyage 64 plankton hauls were taken with "full speed nets" which were towed for an estimated two miles on each occasion.

The biological collections appear to have gone initially to Harvey Johnston's department at the University of Adelaide and from here were sent to experts to be worked up. Some, at least, then remained at the experts' institutions. Thus, some of the fishes sent to J.R. Norman were deposited in the collections of the British Museum (Natural History), while the ascidians sent to Patricia Kott were retained at the C.S.I.R.O. Fisheries Laboratory at Cronulla, New South Wales.

The scientific results were published in a series of B.A.N.Z.A.R.E. Reports which appeared between 1937 and the early 1970s, though by no means all of the collections have yet been worked up. It is expected that the material will eventually be deposited in the South Australian Museum in Adelaide. Mawson's Geographical report was published after his death by Grenfell Price in 1963.

The B.A.N.Z.A.R.E. voyages ended the vessel's sailing career and when she returned to London she was laid up in the East India Docks until she was handed over to the Boy Scouts Association in 1937 to be used as a training ship for Sea Scouts. In this role she moved to the Victoria Embankment where she became a familiar London landmark for more than 40 years.

During the Second World War the ship was used by the Royal Navy for new entry courses and became the headquarters of the River Emergency Services. During this period her engine was scrapped and her rigging was damaged by a barrage balloon.

After the war she reverted to Scout use until her ownership was transferred to the Royal

R.R.S. Discovery, *Victoria Harbour, Dundee, June 1986. Courtesy J. Bryant, Dundee Industrial Heritage.*

Navy in 1955 and she eventually became attached to the London Division of the Royal Naval Reserve. Finally, in 1979 she was transferred to her present owners, the Maritime Trust.

By this time she was in a very sad condition, most of her internal fittings having been removed, though most of the hull was in a remarkably good state. She was accordingly dry docked at Sheerness and extensive restoration work carried out at a total cost of more than £500,000 (cf. her original cost of £33,700!). Essential hull repairs were made and the vessel was completely re-rigged once more as a barque. In this partially restored state *Discovery* was moved to St Katharine's Dock where she was one of a variety of vessels on public display.

In 1985 the Trust concluded an agreement to charter the vessel to the Dundee Industrial Heritage and *Discovery* was transported in March-April 1986 from London to Dundee where her restoration will be completed. She will eventually be placed in a purpose-built berth at Craig Harbour and will form the main feature of a new waterfront development.

References:

Bernacchi, 1938; Fletcher, 1984; Hardy, 1967; Kemp, Hardy and Mackintosh, 1929; Maritime Trust; Price, 1963; Scott, 1905; Thomas, P.M. (pers. comm.); Wilson, 1966.

DISCOVERY II

Steel steam vessel, built 1929 by Ferguson Brothers (Port Glasgow) Ltd., 1036 tons gross, 234' long, 36' beam, 1250 h.p. triple expansion engines. The first British oceanographic research vessel specifically built for this purpose.

The vessel was built for the Discovery Committee to replace their first ship, Scott's *Discovery,* then being used for the B.A.N.Z.A.R. Expedition under Sir Douglas Mawson. The new ship was to continue the investigation of the Southern Ocean along with the *William Scoresby* which was at that time half-way through her first commission.

R.R.S. *Discovery II* sailed from London on her own first commission in December 1929, under the command of W.M. Carey and with the Director of the Discovery Investigations, Stanley Kemp, as chief scientist. The other scientists on board were N.A. Mackintosh, who succeeded Kemp as Director in 1936, H.F.P. Herdman and A.J. Clowes (both chemists), F.C. Fraser who later became Keeper of Zoology at the British Museum (Natural History), and T.J.

R.R.S. Discovery II *off Simonstown, August 1930. Institute of Oceanographic Sciences. Neg. no. 7050.*

Hart, a phytoplanktologist. During this commission, which ended in May 1931, general oceanographic work was conducted, mainly around the Falkland Islands and on the South Georgia whaling grounds, but also in other parts of the South Atlantic and in the Bellingshausen Sea. Surveys of the South Shetlands, South Sandwich Islands, South Georgia and Bouvetøya were also carried out, mainly by A.L. Nelson. A total of 401 stations were worked.

During her second commission, from 1931 to 1933, the vessel was again under the command of Carey, but with Dilwyn John as chief scientist, assisted by J.W.S. Marr, F.D. Ommanney and G.W. Rayner as zoologists, G.E.R. Deacon as chemist, A. Saunders as Deacon's assistant, and with the visiting South African scientist R.S. Veitch. Some 484 stations were worked on a series of lines between the pack ice and ports in the Falklands, South Africa, Australia and New Zealand. This was only the fourth circumnavigation of the Antarctic continent and the first during winter. In addition to the more general survey, much more closely grouped stations were worked around the Falklands and in the northern Weddell Sea.

The third commission, from October 1933 to May 1935, was under the command of Nelson with Mackintosh as chief scientist supported by Hart, Herdman and Clowes, and with Saunders again as assistant. Between December 1933 and November 1934 a series of stations on the 80°W meridian and in the Scotia Sea were visited five times to investigate seasonal changes in the hydrography and the plankton populations. Between these visits to the 80°W line the vessel worked around the Falklands, between South Georgia and South Africa, in the Scotia Sea, in the southern Pacific and between the ice edge and New Zealand. In all, 405 stations were worked. During this commission the *Discovery II* also assisted two land-based antarctic expeditions. First, in early 1934 she carried a doctor and stores from New Zealand for the United States Antarctic Expedition under Admiral R.E. Byrd, making a rendezvous with the Expedition vessel the *Bear of Oakland.* Later, in November 1935, stores and huskies were carried from Port Stanley for the British Graham Land Expedition under John Rymill; the stores were intended for Port Lockroy on Graham Land, but because of the ice conditions encountered they had to be left at Deception Island instead.

The fourth commission, in 1935 to 1937, was under the command of L.R. Hill, with the scientific team consisting of George Deacon, as chief scientist, together with Marr and Ommanney. The original intention was for a circumpolar cruise during the summer months. However, in late November they were diverted to rescue Lincoln Ellsworth and Hollick Kenyon who had been reported missing after leaving Dundee Island off the northern tip of Graham Land in an attempt to fly across the antarctic continent to Little America at the Bay of Whales in the Ross Sea.

Discovery II was working off Enderby Land on the opposite side of Antarctic when the rescue request came. She therefore returned to Melbourne for fuel and to be modified to take two aircraft. When she reached the Bay of Whales on 15 January 1936 the two Americans were found safe and well, the plane having crashed only some fifteen miles short of its objective. *Discovery* returned to Melbourne with Ellsworth, Kenyon having stayed behind to join his own expedition ship, the *Wyatt Earp,* which soon arrived.

The original plan for this commission was now dropped and *Discovery II* instead worked lines of stations across the Indian and Atlantic sectors of the Southern Ocean and in the areas around the Falklands, Balleny Islands, South Georgia and South Orkneys. Finally, the survey of the South Shetland Islands was continued. In all, 482 stations were worked.

The fifth commission, from 1937 to 1939, was again under the command of Hill, with Herdman as chief scientist. The first half of the commission, from November 1937 to May 1938, was occupied in an eastward circumpolar cruise from Cape Town to Cape Town during which 265 stations were worked. After a refit in South Africa a series of seven cruises towards Antarctica were made over more or less the same track between July 1938 and March 1939.

Finally, a series of stations was worked off the West African coast and in the Gulf of Guinea before the ship finally reached London in May 1939.

After the outbreak of war, although the Discovery Investigations continued under the Directorship of Mackintosh, the ships were taken into war service. *Discovery II* was initially fitted out as an Armed Boarding Vessel for service in the Denmark Strait. In 1942 she was taken over by Trinity House and used as a lighthouse tender for five years, followed by a period with the Commissioners for Irish Lights.

In 1944 the Scientific Advisory Committee of the War Cabinet had recommended that a British Oceanographical Institute should be set up as a matter of national importance. During the next four years, discussions between the Royal Society and various Government agencies, including the Admiralty and the Colonial Office, led to the establishment in 1949 of the National Institute of Oceanography. George Deacon became the first Director and Neil Mackintosh the Deputy Director. The new institute took over the work of the Oceanographical Group of the Royal Naval Scientific Service and also the Discovery Investigations, which ceased to be the responsibility of the Falkland Islands Dependencies on 31 March 1949.

Discovery II, along with the *William Scoresby*, was purchased by the Admiralty from the Falklands Government in 1948 and presented to the Institute. The ships were re-fitted and re-equipped, their pre-war equipment having been destroyed during an air-raid in 1940 while in store at St Katharine's Dock in London.

Initially the ships were to continue the pre-war work of the Discovery Investigations in the Southern Ocean so that the early cruises were therefore principally biological. The *William Scoresby* sailed in January 1950, but the *Discovery II* was not ready until May when she sailed from Plymouth under the command of J.F. Blackburn and with Herdman as chief scientist assisted by Roland Cox, Peter David and Peter Foxton.

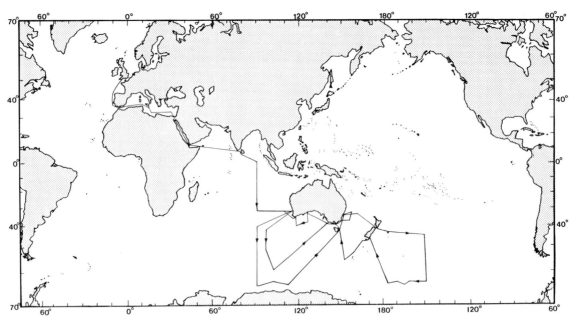

Track of R.R.S. Discovery II *during her first post-war commission, from May 1950 to March 1951. Redrawn from National Institute of Oceanography, Annual Reports for 1950 and 1951.*

The plan was to complete the general survey of the oceanography of the Southern Ocean, begun before the war, and particularly to make observations during the winter months and in parts of the Indian and Pacific sectors which had been omitted from the earlier surveys.

Several stations were worked during the outward voyage to Colombo via the Suez Canal, but the main programme began with a line of stations from the equator to 30°S on the 90°E line of longitude during the passage from Colombo to Fremantle. The vessel now undertook a series of three major antarctic cruises. In August-September 1950, between Fremantle and Sydney, she extended the 90°E line of stations to the ice-edge and worked some stations for the Australian authorities. After working across the Tasman Sea to Wellington she worked a line of stations during November along 150°W, in the Pacific sector, from 45°S to the ice-edge, and also collected samples and data for the New Zealand Government, ending this cruise in Dunedin. Before the third antarctic cruise the ship landed stores at Macquarie Island for an Australian expedition and then made some observations at the Antarctic Convergence before going first to Melbourne and then to Fremantle, carrying out more work for the Australian Government on the way. The third antarctic cruise, from Fremantle to Sydney during February-March 1951, repeated the southern part of the stations worked on 90°E during the previous southern winter.

After refitting, the *Discovery II* left Sydney in May 1951 for a circumpolar voyage, only the second such voyage in winter, the first being her own cruise in 1932. She worked first across the Pacific sector to Port Stanley in the Falklands, then to Simonstown and Durban. Finally, she crossed the Indian Ocean sector to Fremantle via Kerguelen and Heard Island.

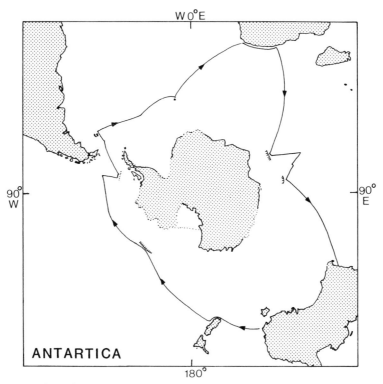

Track of R.R.S. Discovery II *during her circumpolar voyage between May and September 1951, her last visit to antarctic waters. Redrawn from National Institute of Oceanography, Annual Reports for 1950 and 1951.*

The ship left Fremantle for the homeward voyage on 2 October 1951, sailing via Colombo and the Mediterranean to reach Plymouth in December, having worked a number of stations in the Indian Ocean, Red Sea and Mediterranean.

This commission was the last one in which *Discovery II* visited the Antarctic. From her return to the U.K. until she was replaced by the present *Discovery* in 1962, *Discovery II* was employed generally on much shorter cruises, mainly in the North Atlantic. These cruises were much more similar to the modern pattern than those which had gone before. Although biology was still a very important element of the Institute's work, it was no longer the main driving force. Consequently, many cruises were devoted to other disciplines, particularly to geology and geophysics, and the scientists involved included not only N.I.O. personnel, but also representatives from other laboratories and university departments. The work of this period falls outside the scope of this book, but details of it will be found in the published cruise reports and in the Annual Reports of the National Institute of Oceanography.

After 33 years of service to marine science, *Discovery II* was finally broken up at Cobh in Ireland in 1963. The results of the scientific work carried out by *Discovery II,* her predecessor *Discovery* and the *William Scoresby* were reported mainly in the 188 separate papers of the *Discovery Reports,* published between 1929 and 1980.

References:

Ardley and Mackintosh, 1936; Coleman-Cooke, 1963; Hardy, 1967; National Institute of Oceanography, Annual Reports from 1949-1962.

HMS DOROTHEA

Ex-whaler, 382 ton, initially hired, and subsequently purchased by the Navy as a transport to accompany the *Congo* on the ill-fated Tuckey Expedition of 1816 and sent back when the mouth of the River Congo was reached (see under *Congo*).

In 1818 she was used in an expedition under the command of Alexander Buchan in an attempt to penetrate the polar seas north of Spitsbergen accompanied by the *Trent* under John Franklin. The expedition was not a great success since the ships were forced by bad weather and ice conditions to turn back at the edge of the pack. No account of the voyage was published until the appearance in 1843 of the narrative of F.W. Beechey who had sailed as Franklin's First Officer on the *Trent.* Interest at the time seems to have been overshadowed by the controversy surrounding the simultaneous western expedition in the *Isabella* and *Alexander* under John Ross.

H.M.S. Dorothea. Artist F.W. Beechey. A somewhat fanciful representation, typical of Beechey (see also Trent). Courtesy National Maritime Museum. Neg. no. X 182.

HMS EGERIA

"Fantome" class composite screw sloop, 2-7inch, 2-64 pdr, built Pembroke Dock, 1873, 727 (bm), 894 tons displacement, 160' long, 31'6" beam, 120 n.h.p., 1011 i.h.p., complement 76.

The *Egeria* was used as a survey vessel of the Hydrographic Department almost continuously from 1886 to 1910, mainly in the southwestern Pacific and Indian Ocean until 1894 and in the north-eastern Pacific from 1897.

From 1886 to 1888 she was under the command of Pelham Aldrich and in 1887 obtained mineralogical samples from Christmas Island in the Indian Ocean which ultimately led Sir John Murray to establish the Christmas Island Phosphate Company.

From 1890 to 1894 the *Egeria* was under the command of A.M. Field and during this period, in 1893, she was ordered to carry out a survey of Macclesfield Bank in the China Sea to complete the earlier work by the *Rambler* and *Penguin*. P.W. Bassett-Smith, who had been surgeon during the previous surveys and had obtained extensive zoological collections, requested a transfer from *Penguin* to *Egeria* and made further collections which went eventually to the British Museum (Natural History).

H.M.S. Egeria. *Courtesy Imperial War Museum. Neg. no. Q 40950.*

In 1897 the vessel was commissioned for service on the coast of British Columbia by M.H. Smyth. During the passage out observations of the Atlantic Equatorial Current were made using a Pillsbury current-meter acquired by the Admiralty the previous year and used in the Straits of Dover from the *Research*. Smyth recorded a surface current of 0.8 knot, with still water below 10 fathoms (18m). This observation was felt to need confirmation since the reliability of the meter was still suspect as far as the Admiralty was concerned.

During her period in the north-eastern Pacific the *Egeria* worked mainly in relatively shallow water, but in 1899, while under the command of Smyth, she undertook a survey of a projected submarine cable route between Hawaii and Vancouver.

The *Egeria* was eventually sold to the Vancouver Navy League in 1911.

References:
Bassett-Smith, 1895; Burstyn, 1975; Day, 1967; Deacon, 1971; McConnell, 1982; Somerville, 1900.

ENDURANCE

Wooden barquentine-rigged vessel with triple-expansion steam engines, 350 tons, built at Sandefjord, Norway for polar work and originally named *Polaris*. She was purchased for Sir Ernest Shackleton's British Imperial Trans-Antarctic Expedition of 1914-1917 at a cost of £14,000.

After his return from the British Antarctic Expedition on the *Nimrod* from 1907 to 1909 which, though highly successful, had failed to reach the South Pole, Shackleton concluded, correctly, that the Pole would be reached by Amundsen or Scott. He accordingly planned a transcontinental expedition in which he hoped to lead a sledging party from the Weddell Sea, via the Pole, to the Ross Sea where a series of depots were to have been set up by a party carried there on Douglas Mawson's old ship, the *Aurora*. The Weddell Sea party, under the leadership of Shackleton and with Frank Wild the second-in-command, was to be carried by the *Endurance* under the command of Frank A. Worsley. In addition to the terrestrial observations to be

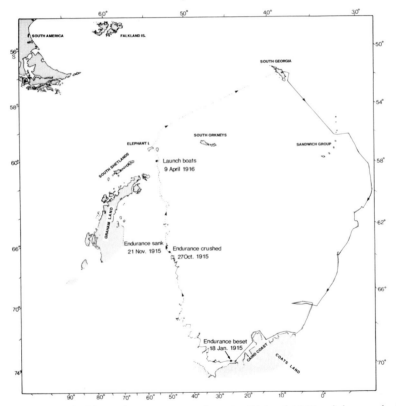

Track of Endurance *during Shackleton's last antarctic expedition in 1914 and 1915 and the route back to South Georgia via Elephant Island. Redrawn from Shackleton, 1919.*

60

Endurance *beset by ice. Courtesy National Maritime Museum. Neg. no. P 11.*

made by the shore parties, both ships were to be equipped for oceanographic work, the *Endurance* being expected to attempt to trace the then unknown coastline of Graham Land. The expedition was financed by contributions from many private individuals and organisations, but particularly by Sir James Caird who donated £24,000, and the British Government which provided £10,000.

The *Endurance* sailed from Plymouth on August 8 1914, three days after the declaration of war, Shackleton having offered the services of both the ship and her personnel to the Admiralty and having been told to proceed with the expedition.

The ship sailed via Buenos Aires to South Georgia where she stayed for a month while the final preparations were made. She left South Georgia on 5 December 1914 and, after visiting the South Sandwich Islands, reached the coast of Coats Land at about 16°W in early January 1915. After surveying about 200 miles of new coastline, named the Caird Coast, the ship was eventually beset in the ice in late January at about 76°30'S. She drifted for 281 days in the ice, reaching a furthest south at about 77°S: 35°W, and then being carried north eventually to be crushed and abandoned on 27 October 1915 at 69°5'S: 51°30'W, some 573 miles from the point where she had become beset, but having covered about 1500 miles. The crew escaped, and after drifting northwards on the ice for a further five months took to the ship's boats, eventually reaching Elephant Island in the South Shetland Islands in April 1916. Shackleton and six others sailed the 800 miles to South Georgia in one of the boats, the *James Caird* (now owned by Dulwich College, in southeast London), and made the first crossing of the island, from King Haakon Bay to the whaling stations at Stromness Bay.

Shackleton then organised a series of relief expeditions during 1916 to attempt to rescue the Elephant Island party. The first three, in the *Southern Sky* in May, the *Instituto de Pesca I* in June, and the *Emma* in July, were unsuccessful, but the fourth expedition, in the Chilean vessel *Yelcho,* reached Elephant Island on 30 August 1916.

The scientific programme originally planned for the expedition clearly could not be carried out, but when it had become obvious that the transcontinental party could not be landed the intended terrestrial observations were made on the ship instead. Consequently, meteorological data were collected throughout the drift by L.D.H. Hussey and magnetic observations were made by R.W. James.

According to J.M. Wordie, officially the geologist of the expedition, the busiest man during the drift was R.S. Clark, the biologist. Before the ship became beset Clark had concentrated on the collection of plankton samples, but during the drift itself he obtained almost daily plankton samples and also made frequent use of the dredge, the deepest haul being at 419 fathoms (766m). In the absence of geological material, apart from the occasional rock retrieved by the dredge, Wordie concentrated on the sea-floor topography, taking frequent soundings and collecting bottom samples. He also made a study of sea ice, and helped Clark with sub-surface temperature and salinity measurements. Unfortunately, the samples collected had to be left behind when the *Endurance* was abandoned.

References:
Shackleton, 1919; Wordie, 1918.

HMS ENTERPRISE

Survey sloop, built at Blackwall 1848, 471 (bm), 126' long, 28'6" beam.

The *Enterprise* was used in the search for Sir John Franklin in 1848-1849 under the command of Sir James Clark Ross, accompanied by E.J. Bird in command of the *Investigator.* The season was a very severe one and Ross was unable to penetrate beyond North Somerset Island where the ships wintered and were not released until late August 1849. When the ships moved north into Barrow Strait, with the intention of sailing westwards, they became locked in the pack ice which carried them east into Lancaster Sound. When they were finally released, in late September, Ross decided to abandon the expedition and returned home to England in November.

During the periods when the ships were ice-bound, Ross made observations on the relation between variations in atmospheric pressure and sea-level. He thought these observations were new, but the relationship had previously been observed by Daussy and Lubbock.

From 1850 to 1859 the *Enterprise* was employed under Richard Collinson in a series of attempts to find evidence of the Franklin Expedition via Bering Strait. The vessel initially sailed in the company of the *Investigator* once more, this time under Robert M'Clure who had been Ross's First Lieutenant in the *Enterprise* during the 1848-49 voyage. However, the two ships became separated in the Pacific and never met up again. The *Investigator* was eventually abandoned at Mercy Bay on Banks Island in 1853, but not until after M'Clure had discovered Prince of Wales Strait leading through to Parry's Melville Sound, reached by the *Hecla* and *Griper* in 1820, and thus proving for the first time that a North-West Passage actually existed.

In the meantime, Collinson in the *Enterprise* had been unable to penetrate beyond Point Barrow in 1850 and had wintered at Hong Kong. However, in 1851 and 1852 the *Enterprise* wintered on the shores of Victoria Island and several sledge journeys were undertaken in search of Franklin, but found only a metal bolt and a section of cabin door frame. In 1853 Collinson sailed west and wintered at Camden Bay in Alaska, returning to England in 1854 after having met the *Plover* at Point Barrow. In addition to the geographical discoveries, meteorological, ethnological and biological observations had been made, but apart from some data on surface currents no significant oceanographic information was obtained.

The *Enterprise* became a coal hulk in 1860 and eventually was sold in 1903.

References:

Bockstoce, 1985; Collinson, 1889; Deacon, 1971; Dodge, 1973; Jones, 1971; Kirwan, 1959; M'Clure, 1857; Ross, 1854.

HMS EREBUS

"Hecla" class bomb vessel, 1-13inch and 1-10inch mortars, 2-6 pdr, 8-24 pdr carronades, built at Pembroke Dock 1826, 372 (bm), 105' long, 28'6" beam, design complement 67.

The *Erebus* had seen only two years of service, in the Mediterranean from 1828 to 1830, before she was selected, along with the *Terror,* for the antarctic expedition of 1839-1843 under the command of James Clark Ross.

The main scientific objectives of the expedition were to measure the earth's magnetic field in the southern hemisphere and to locate the south magnetic pole. This work was to include observations made on specific predetermined days for comparison with similar observations to be made at the same time at various other localities. Pressure for the undertaking came principally from the British Association for the Advancement of Science, and particularly from its Secretary Edward Sabine, but the recommendation also received the support of the Royal Society.

In addition to the magnetic work, which was to involve the establishment of land observatories in addition to measurements at sea, the expedition was to undertake physical, meteorological, geological and biological programmes. From a specifically oceanographic point of view, Ross was to obtain surface and sub-surface temperature measurements, deep-soundings and marine biological collections whenever the opportunity presented itself.

Ross took command of the *Erebus,* while the *Terror* was under the command of Francis R.M.

Crozier. As was usual for such voyages of the time, no specialist scientists were carried. However, the surgeon on the *Erebus*, Robert McCormick, who had been the official surgeon-naturalist on the *Beagle* with Darwin but had returned home after falling out with Fitzroy, was also the official naturalist, while the Assistant Surgeon, Joseph Dalton Hooker, was in effect aboard because of his botanical interests.

The ships sailed from England on 30 September 1839 and, after establishing shore-based observatories at St. Helena and the Cape, and visiting Kerguelen Island, they arrived at Hobart, Tasmania in August 1840. At Hobart they met Sir John Franklin, Ross's old friend and arctic companion who had been Governor since 1836. They were not to know then, of course, that the fates of Franklin and Crozier were to be tragically linked with those of the two ships. In Tasmania a third observatory was set up, with its staff including Joseph Dayman who had sailed as a mate in the *Erebus* and was later to have a distinguished surveying career (see, for instance, *Cyclops, Gorgon* and *Firebrand*).

H.M.S. Erebus *and* Terror *in Peel Sound in 1846 during Sir John Franklin's Expedition. Artist M. Myers, 1977. Reproduced with the kind permission of Mr. Richard Noyes Roberts and the artist. National Maritime Museum Neg. no. C211.*

After extensive refitting, the ships sailed on 12 November 1840 for the Auckland Islands. Here a temporary observatory was established and several days of observations were made, including one of the predetermined term days, before they left once more on 17 December and sailed due south. They crossed the Antarctic Circle and reached the edge of the pack ice on New Year's Day 1841 and passed through the ice into open water, later to be named the Ross Sea, on 9 January.

Having observed Victoria Land at Cape Adare and sailed down the eastern coast, Mounts Erebus and Terror and the Ice Barrier were discovered on 28 January, Mount Erebus actively erupting. With no possibility of sailing westwards, towards the south magnetic pole, Ross decided to explore the extent of the Ice Barrier, following it for some 300 miles before turning back in search of possible winter quarters. No suitable quarters were found and the decision to turn north was taken on 16 February. After an eventful and hazardous voyage during which extensive magnetic observations were made, together with some deep soundings and sub-surface temperature measurements, the vessels returned to Tasmania on 6 April 1841. It was during this section of the voyage that Ross sailed through the position of land marked by Wilkes north of Balleny Island on a chart prepared during the United States Exploring Expedition and received by Ross at Hobart in August 1840. This was the source of the major disagreement between Ross and Wilkes and of the controversy about Wilkes' discoveries which raged for well over a century (see Ross, 1982).

After refitting, the vessels left Hobart on 7 July 1841 for a visit to Sydney for magnetometric observations for comparison with those made in Tasmania. The ships then sailed to New Zealand where extensive magnetic and pendulum observations were made, while McCormick and Hooker made geological and biological collections.

On 23 November 1841 the *Erebus* and *Terror* left the Bay of Islands for the second antarctic voyage in which Ross intended to investigate the Antarctic land mass further to the east than had been possible in the previous season. He attempted to penetrate the pack ice at about 145°W, but was forced by ice conditions much further to the west and eventually investigated the eastern end of the Ross Ice Barrier, possibly seeing what Scott later named King Edward VII Land, but recording only "the appearance of land". During this voyage the vessels reached 78°10′S, a record which stood for almost 60 years, and sailed along the Barrier some 10° further east than previously.

After retreating from the Barrier in late February Ross sailed north to the 60° parallel and thence eastward towards the Falklands. Ross believed that they were clear of ice at this latitude, but in the early hours of 13 March 1841 they encountered enormous icebergs. In a gale the two ships collided but both managed to slip through a narrow passage between two particularly large bergs, escaping destruction by a combination of good luck and good seamanship. After repairing the damage they continued eastward and ultimately reached the Falklands on 5 April, sighting land for the first time in 136 days.

During the winter of 1842 astronomical, meteorological and magnetometric observations were conducted on the Falklands and a short visit was made to Cape Horn to carry out similar observations for comparison with the Falklands results. Finally, on 17 December 1842 the ships left Port Louis for the third and final antarctic voyage.

The intention this time was to penetrate well into the Weddell Sea, but after sighting Joinville Island, off the tip of the Graham Land peninsula, and discovering and taking possession of the James Ross Island Group, Ross encountered particularly severe ice conditions which impeded his southerly progress. Nevertheless, the ships reached 71°30′S on 5 March 1843 by which time they were no more than 45 miles from Queen Maud Land which was not finally discovered until 1932. Two days earlier, and not far to the north, Ross had found no bottom with 4000 fathoms of sounding line out, giving rise to the mythical Ross Deep which was not removed from charts until after the turn of the present century (see *Scotia*).

Unable to proceed further south, Ross made for the Cape of Good Hope, unsuccessfully trying to locate Bouvetøya (Bouvet Island) during the passage, though he must have passed within a few miles of it. After reaching Simonstown on 4 April the ships sailed once more on 30 April and, after making further magnetic observations at St Helena, Ascension and Rio, finally anchored off Folkestone on 4 September 1843.

In its primary objective, the measurement of the earth's magnetic field in the southern hemisphere, the expedition had been a great success, though it took Edward Sabine twenty-five years to publish all of the results! Similarly, very considerable geographical advances had been made, particularly in the Ross Sea area, for although Ross never claimed to have obtained conclusive evidence for the existence of a major antarctic land mass, his charting of some 500 miles of the coast of Victoria Land and most of the Ross Ice Barrier was a major achievement.

Thirdly, Hooker's botanical collection made during the voyage led to the publication of his superb six-volume work on the *Botany of the Antarctic voyage of H.M. discovery ships Erebus and Terror. . .* which appeared between 1847 and 1860 and established his reputation as a taxonomist and phytogeographer. In the first of these volumes, *Flora Antarctica,* the only one entirely based on the *Erebus* and *Terror* work, Hooker emphasized the ubiquitous occurrence of diatoms in his townet samples in antarctic waters, in ooze samples collected off the Ice Barrier, and in samples of discoloured ice. Many of these samples had been examined by the German microscopist Christian Ehrenberg and formed the subject of an appendix to Ross's general account of the expedition.

Although Ross devoted a great deal of effort to the acquisition of oceanographic data throughout the voyage, the results were equivocal in all three of the main topics which he tackled, the measurement of sub-surface temperatures, deep-sea soundings and the collection of biologial samples.

For deep-sea temperatures Ross was provided with Six maximum-minimum thermometers, but was not warned of the erroneous readings which such instruments were prone to give because of the distortion caused by the high pressure at great depth. Nor was Ross told of a letter from Alexander von Humboldt to the First Lord of the Admiralty pointing out the error of the widely held belief that sea water, like fresh water, had a maximum density at about 4°C. This letter arrived after the *Erebus* and *Terror* left England, but it was actually printed with Ross's instructions when these were published in 1840.

Throughout the voyage Ross made sub-surface temperature measurements down to a depth of 600 fathoms (1097m) during the first season, but subsequently to twice this depth after stronger thermometers were sent out to him in June 1841. Because Ross was using unprotected thermometers he never recorded temperatures lower than 39.5°F. He therefore felt that the results supported the so-called "4°C theory", according to which the whole of the deep sea was filled with water at this temperature, most recently and most forcefully expounded by Dumont d'Urville following his voyage in the *Astrolabe* in 1826-1829. This theory was not finally discredited until the cruise of the *Lightning* in 1868 and Ross's results certainly contributed to its continuance long after contrary evidence was available (see also under *Isabella* and *Hydra*). As an extension of the ideas embodied in the theory, Ross reported the existence of a "circle of mean temperature" at about 56°S where, he believed, the water temperature was 39.5°F throughout the water column. Ross thought that this zone separated what he called "the two great thermic basins of the oceans", the surface waters to the north being warmer than the "mean" temperature while those to the south were colder. Deacon (1971) has pointed out that Ross's "circle. . ." coincides very closely with the Antarctic Convergence where cold polar water meets warm water from lower latitudes and sinks beneath it, so that Ross was right to think that this was an important region, but for the wrong reasons!

Ross made numerous relatively shallow soundings, down to a few hundreds of fathoms, but also several very deep soundings using the ships' boats in an attempt to avoid the problems of drifting to which the ships themselves were more prone. The rate at which the line ran out was determined by timing the passage of each one hundred fathoms, and the arrival of the weight on the sea-floor was detected by a marked slowing in this rate. Most of the deep soundings were at about 2000 fathoms and at this depth Ross's technique could be quite accurate. Thus, the position of his first deep sounding, at 2425 fathoms (4413m) in the South Atlantic during the outward voyage, was re-surveyed by the U.S.S. *Discoverer* in 1968 and found to be 2100 fathoms (3822m) deep. However, the check as the weight reached the bottom could be very difficult to discern, leading to erroneously deep soundings. In March 1843, for instance, deep in the Weddell Sea and shortly before he had to turn back and head for the Cape, Ross made a sounding with 4000 fathoms (7316m) of line, apparently without reaching the bottom. This sounding was entered onto the charts where it remained, as the Ross Deep, until the *Scotia* recorded a depth of 2660 fathoms (4840m) only about two miles away during the Scottish National Antarctic Expedition in 1902-1904. Ross's timing figures for this sounding were re-examined by R.T. Gould in 1924 and a slight check, which Ross has missed, was detected at 2200 fathoms (c. 4000m), a figure not inconsistent with the *Scotia* results. Ross made a similarly erroneous sounding in June 1843, this time with 4600 fathoms of line, some 500 miles north-east of Trinidad during the homeward voyage.

Ross's deep-sea biological work was much less extensive. The tow-net could be used without too much trouble and seems to have been deployed quite frequently, but the effort involved in fishing a dredge at great depth, without the assistance of a powered capstan, was enormous. Nevertheless, the dredge was used several times in deep water including once at a depth of 400 fathoms (730m) north-west of North Cape, New Zealand. The presence of animals in all of the dredge catches led Ross to conclude that ". . .from however great a depth we may be enabled to bring up the mud and stones of the bed of the ocean, we shall find them teeming with animal life. . ." thus directly contradicting Edward Forbes' influential azoic theory which was based largely on his own work in the Mediterranean at more or less the same time as the *Erebus* and *Terror* voyage (see under *Beacon*).

Ross's results might have had a greater influence in preventing the general acceptance of the azoic theory if they had been properly reported, but they were not. The zoological results appeared in two volumes edited by Sir John Richardson, Hooker's old teacher at the Royal Naval Hospital, Haslar, and J.E. Gray, Keeper of Zoology at the British Museum, and containing a series of papers published between 1844 and 1875, subsidised by a grant of £1,000 from the Admiralty. Most of these reports dealt with the vertebrate groups and included collections and information other than those obtained from the *Erebus* and *Terror*. Richardson's own account of the fishes was a very significant contribution to knowledge of the ichthyology of the regions visited, and was based almost entirely upon collections made during the voyage, but the author bemoaned the state of many of the specimens following their long sojourn on the ships. Richardson included a sketch by John Robertson, the surgeon of the *Terror*, of a small fish which was found embedded in a thick layer of ice on the ship's bows after several days of intensely cold and stormy weather in February 1842 during the second antarctic voyage. Richardson was sure that the fish was of a previously unknown species, but Robertson's drawing was insufficiently detailed for him to determine its relationships; the specimen itself had been eaten by the ship's cat!

Pagetodes. John Robertson's sketch of the fish found frozen to the bows of H.M.S. Terror *and later eaten by the ship's cat (see text). Reproduced from Richardson, 1844-48.*

The *Zoology* volumes contained only two short papers on the marine invertebrates, one by E.J. Miers on the crustaceans, and a second by Adam White on the molluscs. Otherwise the dredged samples seem to have gone largely unreported, mainly because Ross retained the specimens, intending to work them up himself. He never managed to do so and the collections, by then largely destroyed, were eventually found by Hooker in the back garden of Ross's house in Aylesbury after his death in 1862.

After their return from the Antarctic Expedition, and having proved their suitability for polar exploration, the *Erebus* and *Terror* were selected for a further assault on the North-West Passage. At the suggestion of Sir Edward Parry, by this time Comptroller of Steam Machinery for the Navy, they were fitted with retractable screws and auxiliary 20 h.p. steam engines adapted from railway locomotives on the London and Greenwich and London and Birmingham lines. Apart from the curious origin of the engines, this modification of the *Erebus* and *Terror* was remarkable also because the two vessels thus became the first naval ships with bladed screws, rather than Archimedean screws as fitted to the four earlier screw vessels.

The expedition sailed from Chatham in May 1845 under the command of Sir John Franklin in the *Erebus* and with Crozier once more in command of the *Terror*. In late June, Harry Goodsir, the naturalist on the *Erebus,* obtained abundant animals in dredge hauls to a depth of 300 fathoms (550m) in Davis Strait and wrote to inform his friend Edward Forbes when they called at Disco in Greenland. Franklin sailed into Lancaster Sound and eventually wintered at Beechey Island. In the spring of 1846 the ships sailed south-west along Peel Sound, between Somerset Island and Prince of Wales Island, into Franklin Strait and became beset in the pack ice of Victoria Strait west of King William Island. They failed to become free during the summer of 1847 and Franklin died in June that year. After a further winter in the ice the ships were abandoned in April 1848, Crozier attempting to take the surviving men to Great Fish (now Back) River. None survived, and their tragic story gradually came to light over the next one hundred and forty years, the remarkably well preserved body of one member of the party being uncovered as recently as 1984.

The ships were never with certainty seen again, and contemporary Eskimo stories suggested that they were crushed and sunk. However, in 1851 two reported sightings were made from merchant vessels of two ships, fitting the description of the *Erebus* and *Terror,* drifting on or close to icebergs off Newfoundland. The vessels were never identified, but it has been suggested that they were indeed Franklin's ships carried some 2000 miles from their position when they were abandoned.

References:

Cyriax, 1939; Deacon, 1971; Dietz and Knebel 1968; Gould, 1924; Hooker, 1847; Huxley, L. 1918; Lewis, 1971; Lloyd, 1970; Ritchie, 1967; Ross, J.C. 1847; Ross, M.J. 1982; Savours and McConnell, 1982; Schuessler, 1986; Taylor, 1980.

ESK

Whitby whaler built in 1813 and commanded by William Scoresby Jnr until 1817. During this period Scoresby continued his scientific observations begun in the *Resolution,* initially under his father's command, but under his own captaincy in 1811 and 1812.

Scoresby had come under the influence of Robert Jameson during his time at the University of Edinburgh where Jameson was the professor of natural history, and of Sir Joseph Banks, President of the Royal Society, whom Scoresby had met in London in 1807.

Encouraged by Banks, Scoresby began to make measurements of temperature and specific gravity at various depths in the sea. Initially Scoresby apparently collected subsurface samples with a wooden cask with valves top and bottom similar to the "bucket" designed by the Reverend Stephen Hales about 1750 (see McConnell, 1982). However, water at depth penetrated the wood and caused it to split. Accordingly, Banks had a new apparatus made for him consisting of a brass-bound wooden cask, with valves as in Hales' bucket but with a Six self-

The whaler Esk. *Artist R.K. Greville, published in Scoresby, 1820. Courtesy National Maritime Museum. Neg. no. X 709. During the 1816 voyage to the Greenland whale fishery the* Esk *was holed by the ice and a length of the keel was detached, preventing the application of a fothering sail to stop the leak. The illustration shows Scoresby's unsuccessful attempt to turn the vessel over to get to the keel. Eventually the damaged section of keel was removed and the hole blocked while the ship was upright.*

registering thermometer fastened inside it and with glass windows to allow the thermometer to be read in position.

Scoresby took Banks' apparatus to sea with him in the *Resolution* in 1811. It suffered from the same problems as the earlier one and the valves leaked, but the thermometer worked admirably. He therefore had a similar instrument made, his marine diver, but this time cast in brass. Scoresby apparently used the diver frequently during his voyages in the *Esk,* sometimes with wire gauze fixed across the upper opening so that small organisms which entered through the lower opening were trapped. He also sent samples of wood and other materials down inside the diver to examine the effects of high pressure upon them. It was during such an experiment, in the Greenland Sea on 28 June 1817, that the diver was lost. It had been lowered to a depth of 7200 feet (2195m) and was being carefully hauled in when the line parted with 1050 fathoms (1922m) still out, losing, Scoresby estimated, rope and equipment valued at £20!

On this 1817 expedition Scoresby found the Greenland coast unusually clear of ice and this information ultimately led to the 1818 voyages in search of a north-west passage (see under *Isabella*). Banks tried unsuccessfully to obtain command of one of the ships involved for Scoresby, but it became a naval expedition in which Greenland captains would be employed only as sailing masters or advisers and Scoresby was unwilling to act in this capacity.

Instead, Scoresby made a further whaling voyage, this time in command of the *Fame,* a vessel which William Scoresby Snr had purchased in the conviction that his son would be offered the command of the north-west passage expedition. At the end of this voyage the two Scoresbys fell out and their long-standing partnership came to an end. Scoresby junior eventually entered into a one third partnership with two Liverpool businessmen which resulted in the building, under Scoresby's superintendence, of the *Baffin* in which he undertook his last four voyages to the Greenland whale fishery and continued his oceanographic observations.

References:

Deacon, 1971; McConnell, 1982; Stamp and Stamp, 1976.

HMS EURYDICE

"Porcupine" class 6th rate vessel, 22-9 pdr, 2-6 pdr, built Portsmouth Dockyard 1781, 521 (bm), 114'3" long, 32' beam, design complement 160.

In 1816 Capt. Robert Wauchope in command of the *Eurydice* attempted to measure the temperature at great depth at 3°26'S: 7°59'E using an insulated Hales' bucket consisting of a series of five tin cases and an outer wooden case. The space between the wooden case and the first tin container was filled with tallow and each case had an upward opening valve at the top and bottom to allow free flow of water during descent.

The bucket was lowered on 1435 fathoms of rope, but from the angle adopted by the line as a result of the ship's drift Wauchope estimated that it reached a depth of about 1000 fathoms (1830m). Wauchope reported that it took 22 minutes to lower the bucket, but "it took a hundred men just one hour and twenty minutes. . ." to retrieve it!

The temperature recorded was 42°F, while the surface temperature was 73°F.

The *Eurydice* was hulked at Woolwich in 1824 and was broken up in 1834.

References:
Deacon, 1971; Wauchope, 1822.

HMS FAIRY

"Cherokee" class brig, 2-6 pdr carronades, 8-18 pdr carronades, built Chatham Dockyard 1826, 235 (bm), 90' long, 24'6" beam.

The *Fairy* was commissioned as a survey vessel in December 1831 for work in the North Sea, the previous vessel employed in this service, the gun-brig *Protector,* having become inadequate. William Hewett, who had been in command of the *Protector* since 1818, took command of the *Fairy.*

Hewett's tidal observations in the *Fairy* confirmed William Whewell's prediction of the existence in the North Sea of an amphidrome, a region where there is almost no tidal rise and fall in sea level.

In November 1840 the *Fairy* was lost with all hands in a gale off the Suffolk coast and was replaced by the *Shearwater.*

References:
Dawson, 1885; Day, 1967; Deacon, 1971; Gossett, 1986.

FINGAL

Schooner-rigged steam yacht, 110' long, 17'9" beam, 158 tons gross, with a 200 h.p. engine, chartered by the Royal Dublin Society to carry out a survey of the fishing grounds of the southern and western coasts of Ireland from May to August 1890. This was to be the first part of a two year survey at an estimated total cost of £1,200. The financial arrangement was that the Government would pay half of this cost, but since the actual cost considerably exceeded the estimate the Society in the end paid for well over half of the survey.

The *Fingal* had originally been built as a private yacht, but at the time of the Irish survey she was employed during the winter as a North Sea long liner.

The Expedition was under the leadership of the Rev. W.S. Green, with Prof. A.C. Haddon of the Royal College of Science as naturalist and T.H. Poole as second in command of the expedition and to take responsibility for the temperature and specific gravity observations. Haddon was not able to participate in the whole cruise because of his collegiate duties and his place during the early part of the survey was taken by various other naturalists including E.W.L. Holt who joined the ship in early June.

The main sampling gear used was a 25′ beam trawl, but the *Fingal* also carried an otter trawl, an Agassiz trawl and a variety of dredges. The survey covered the coast from Dursey Head in West Cork to Malin Head. A total of 121 stations was worked and although most of the catches were obtained in relatively shallow water, one haul was made at a depth of 900m.

The *Fingal* was not available for the survey in 1891 and the work was therefore continued in the *Harlequin.*

References:

Department of Agriculture and Technical Instruction for Ireland, 1902; Holt, 1892; Green, 1890-1891; Le Danois, 1948; Went, 1972.

HMS FIREBRAND

"Cyclops" class paddle frigate, built Portsmouth Dockyard 1842, 1,190 (bm), 190′ long, 37′ beam, 410 n.h.p. engines built by Seawards of Millwall. The vessel was originally to have been called the *Beelzebub,* but was renamed during building.

The *Firebrand* was used in 1859 to make deep soundings in the Bay of Biscay and Mediterranean under the command of Joseph Dayman following his earlier sounding voyages in the *Cyclops* and *Gorgon.*

Dayman used a relatively light line for the soundings which, as on the *Gorgon,* generally parted during hauling in. An attempt to determine the specific gravity of sea water at depth

H.M.S. Firebrand. *Artist H.J. Vernon. Courtesy National Maritime Museum. Neg. no. 4817.*

was made by weighing cubes of wood in surface water after having become sodden at the test depth.

Dayman also tested William Siemens' first "bathometer", in effect a gravimeter which Siemens hoped would measure the depth without the necessity of conventional sounding. The experiments were not a success because Dayman had difficulty in keeping the ice necessary to maintain the bathometer at a constant temperature. In the event, the later versions of the bathometer used on the *Faraday* in the North Sea and Atlantic also were not very successful because Siemens was unable to allow for the complex gravitational effects of the underlying rocks.

The *Firebrand* was sold in 1864.

References:

Dayman, 1860; Gardiner, 1979; Laing, 1980; McConnell, 1982.

HMS FLY

"Fly" class sloop, 16-32 pdr carronades, 2-9 pdr carronades, built Pembroke Dock 1831, 480 (bm), 114′4″ long, 31′4″ beam, design complement 120.

From 1841 to 1846 the *Fly* was employed under Capt. Francis P. Blackwood in surveying in the south-western Pacific and particularly on the Great Barrier Reef, a principal objective being the charting of a safe route through the reef for naval vessels on passage to Sydney. The *Fly*

H.M.S. Fly *at Sydney. Courtesy National Maritime Museum. Neg. no. 8437.*

72

was accompanied by the *Bramble* and, from 1845, by the *Castlereagh* as tenders.

In addition to charting large tracts of the Great Barrier Reef, Blackwood supervised the construction of the Raine Island beacon to mark the "Blackwood Channel" through the outer reef. The beacon, a 70 foot high structure of wood and coral rock blocks cemented together with lime made by burning giant clam (Tridacna) shells, was built with the help of convicts from Sydney.

The *Fly* carried two naturalists, a zoologist, J.W. McGillivray, employed by the Earl of Derby, and a geologist, J. Beete Jukes. The two men appear to have made separate extensive natural history collections, but both sets eventually went to the British Museum.

The *Fly* became a coal hulk at Plymouth in 1855 and was broken up in 1903.

References:
Dawson, 1885; Jukes, 1847; Ritchie, 1967.

FLYING FALCON (see LORD BANDON)

HMS FLYING FISH

"Fantome" class composite screw sloop, built Chatham Dockyard 1873, 727 (bm), 894 tons displacement, 160' long, 31'6" beam, 120 n.h.p., 836 i.h.p., complement 125.

The *Flying Fish* was originally to have been named *Daring*, but her name was changed during building. She was completed as a survey vessel in 1880 and from 1880 to 1883 was employed in surveying in far eastern waters under Lieut. R.F. Hoskyn. From 1883 to the end of 1886 she remained in the far east under the command of Capt. J.F.L.P. Maclear who had been second-in-

H.M.S. Flying Fish. *Reproduced by permission of the Hydrographer to the Navy.*

command to G.S. Nares during the *Challenger* expedition.

At the end of this commission the *Flying Fish* was ordered to return home via Christmas Island in the Indian Ocean, where Maclear collected samples of beach rocks and coral for John Murray who was continuing his interest in coral reefs begun during the *Challenger* voyage. Maclear's samples turned out to be rich in calcium phosphate and prompted Murray to request further samples which were collected by Pelham Aldrich in the *Egeria* in 1887 and ultimately led to the establishment of the Christmas Island Phosphate Company.

During the voyage through the Indian Ocean, Maclear obtained a series of some 43 deep soundings in the neighbourhood of Christmas Island and between Ceylon and the Gulf of Aden to a depth of over 3000 fathoms (c. 5490m). Along with these soundings, Maclear took some near bottom temperatures and numerous bottom samples which were reported on by John Murray (1887) as "the best series of deposits that have as yet been preserved from this Ocean."

The *Flying Fish* was sold in 1888.

References:
Burstyn, 1975; Deacon, 1971; Murray, 1887.

FLYING FOX

Paddle steamer built South Shields by J.T. Eltringham in 1885, 122' long, 20' beam, 174 tons gross, 98 n.h.p.

Green (1889) gave a brief report of a six-day trawling cruise off southern Ireland during July 1889 undertaken in a vessel referred to as the *Flying Fox* to obtain specimens for the British Museum. He lists nine stations, in depths ranging from 40 to 920 fathoms (73 to 1684m) at which successful hauls were made with either an Agassiz trawl or a beam trawl, using wire rope. Green's report is accompanied by brief accounts of the fishes, molluscs, crustaceans, echinoderms, polyzoans, hydrozoans, sponges, radiolarians and foraminiferans.

In his account of the trawling cruise of the *Research,* which took place in the same general area a week or two later, Bourne (1889-90) also refers to the *Flying Fox.* However, it seems possible that both Green and Bourne were mistaken and that the vessel actually used was the very similar *Flying Falcon,* also built by Eltringham and originally named the *Lord Bandon.*

Green had already participated in three cruises in this vessel, two as the *Lord Bandon* in 1885 and 1886, and a third in 1888 after she had been renamed. For the second and third of these cruises the ship had been hired from the Clyde Shipping Company who still owned the vessel in 1889. Green (p. 419) says that for the 1889 cruise he "entered into negotiations with the Clyde Shipping Company, and chartered their steamer the 'Flying Fox' for a week's trip, her skipper, Captain Tobin, and his crew being the same I had worked with on former occasions." In Lloyd's register for 1889, however, the *Flying Fox* is listed under the ownership of G.J. Kidston. I have been unable to resolve the ambiguities in this situation further.

References:
Bourne, 1889-90; Green, 1889.

HMS FROLIC

"Frolic" class brig, 2-18 pdr, 10-32 pdr, built Portsmouth Dockyard 1842, 511 (bm), 108'3" long, 34' beam, design complement 110-130.

In 1854 Alfred Russell Wallace was granted a free passage in the *Frolic* to Singapore after

H.M.S. Frolic, *driven ashore in Brazil. Artist H.J. Vernon. Courtesy National Maritime Museum. Neg. no. 453.*

having spent four years collecting in South America and having lost most of his specimens when the *Helen,* in which he was returning to England, caught fire and sank. In the event, Wallace travelled to Singapore by the so-called 'Overland Route', via Alexandria and Aden, because the *Frolic's* voyage was cancelled and she was instead used as a transport to the Crimea. The *Frolic* made no recorded contribution to oceanography, but during his temporary stay on board Wallace found that her captain, Commander Nolloth, had made private preparations to take deep sea soundings during the voyage, illustrating the interest in obtaining such soundings, generated during the 1840s and 1850s, even among non-surveying officers.

The *Frolic* was sold in 1864 and broken up in 1865.

References:
Deacon, 1971; Williams-Ellis, 1966.

HMS FURY

"Hecla" class bomb vessel, 2 mortars, 2-6 pdr, 8-24 pdr carronades, built Rochester 1814, 372 (bm), 105′ long, 28′6″ beam, design complement 67.

Stoutly built bomb vessels, specifically designed to carry mortars to be employed principally for coastal bombardments, first appeared in the Royal Navy in the late seventeenth century. Additional bombs were built or converted sporadically during the next 150 years, generally in response to a sudden need. In the intervals between these periods of specific requirement they were sometimes employed as ordinary warships, but in the eighteenth century their suitability for polar exploration was appreciated because of their strength and relatively high carrying capacity. From an oceanographic point of view the most important of these eighteenth century bombs were the *Carcass* and *Racehorse* employed for Constantine Phipps' arctic expedition in 1773 during which sub-surface temperature measurements and the first reliable deep-sea soundings were made.

During the nineteenth century several bombs were employed in polar exploration and more general surveying, often being used in these roles much more extensively than for their primary warlike purpose. The *Erebus* and *Terror* are the most famous of these, but they also included the *Hecla, Aetna, Sulphur, Thunder* and the *Beacon,* originally named the *Meteor.*

The *Terror, Hecla* and *Fury* were all built in the 1813 to 1815 period and initially saw action, the *Terror* being sent to America while the *Hecla* and *Fury* took part in the bombardment of Algiers in 1816. After their return from Algiers the *Hecla* was selected for W.E. Parry's first arctic expedition in search of a North-West Passage in company with the gun brig *Griper,* while the *Fury* was laid up in ordinary. The *Griper* turned out to be very unsatisfactory for this work and Parry therefore commissioned the *Fury* for his second expedition in 1821 to 1823, command of the *Hecla* being given to G.F. Lyon. This expedition was much less successful than the first, though it did demonstrate the absence of a North-West Passage from Hudson Strait (see under *Hecla*).

Parry's experiences during his first expedition, and during John Ross's 1818 voyage when he had been in command of the *Alexander,* had led to him to be rather critical of the oceanographic techniques available. Consequently, little significant oceanographic work was carried out during the second expedition, nor during his third voyage when the *Fury* and *Hecla* were again selected, Parry returning to the command of the *Hecla* while Henry Hoppner took the *Fury.*

This time Parry was to proceed via Lancaster Sound to Prince Regent Inlet as on his 1819 expedition, but it was a disaster. Having sailed from England in May 1824, Parry had great difficulty in penetrating the young ice in Lancaster Sound, but eventually wintered at Port Bowen on the eastern shore of Prince Regent Inlet. When the ships were released in 1825 they crossed the Inlet in search of a passage to the west. On August 1 both vessels were forced aground by the ice, the *Fury* sustaining extensive damage in getting off. When she was beached at Fury Beach on Somerset Island and unloaded in order to investigate the extent of the damage, it was found to be so serious that Parry finally abandoned her on 25 August and returned home in October.

References:
Parry, A. 1963; Parry, W.E. 1824, 1826; Pearsall, 1973.

HMS GANNET

Wooden screw sloop, 11-32 pdr, built Pembroke Dock 1857, 579 (bm), 800 tons displacement, 151′ long, 29′ beam, 150 n.h.p.

In 1865 the *Gannet* and the *Serpent* were commissioned as men-o-war with surveying duties as a secondary role in an experiment at combining the two functions. From 1865 to 1868 the *Gannet* was assigned to the North American and West Indies station under the command of William Chimmo. The experiment was not successful and was not continued after the *Gannet* paid off, though the surveying work of Chimmo, and of Lieut. W. J. L. Wharton who later became Hydrographer, was highly regarded.

On the homeward voyage in 1868 Chimmo was ordered to investigate the Gulf Stream and to define its northern limits, taking sub-surface temperature measurements, soundings, and townet samples within the limits of the Stream. The *Gannet* was apparently one of several survey vessels supplied in 1868 with newly designed thermometers, prepared by a variety of instrument makers, hopefully protected against the effects of pressure (see also

Hydra).   However, as Deacon (1971) has pointed out, there is no evidence that Chimmo's Gulf Stream temperatures were taken with protected instruments, although he does refer in his account to the use of "new and delicate thermometers".   On one occasion he recorded a temperature of 39.5°F at a depth of 1000 fathoms (1830m), but mostly he recorded temperatures of no less than 42°F even at depths of 2000 fathoms (3860m).

Chimmo used a Brooke sounding rod for a series of thirteen soundings in depths ranging from 80 to 2700 fathoms (146 to 4938m), and in doing so removed several reported shoal areas from the Admiralty charts.   The Foraminifera and coccoliths brought up in the bottom sediment samples obtained were carefully examined.   With two doubtful exceptions, Chimmo found no evidence that these organisms had lived on the sea-floor, a very controversial matter at the time and one which was not finally resolved until John Murray's careful observations of mid-water samples during the *Challenger* Expedition.

The *Gannet* was eventually sold in 1876.

References:
Chimmo, 1869, 1870; Day, 1967; Deacon, 1971; Ritchie, 1967.

Fisheries Research Vessel Garland. *Reproduced from International Council for the Exploration of the Sea, 1928.*

GARLAND

Iron screw schooner, built 1880 at Dumbarton, 36 tons net, 61 tons gross, 84'6" long between perpendiculars, 15' beam, 14 n.h.p.   The *Garland* was used for fisheries research for the Scottish Fishery Board from 1886 to 1902 after which she was replaced by the *Goldseeker*.

The *Garland* was unsuitable for deep-sea work and her fishing operations were not comparable with those of commercial vessels since she was equipped only with a small beam trawl.   Nevertheless, the statistics which the Fishery Board kept, based on the *Garland's* work, were used as a model for the collection of statistics recommended by the International Council for the Exploration of the Sea at the preliminary conference at Stockholm in 1899.

Reference:
International Council for the Exploration of the Sea, 1928.

HMS GOLDFINCH

"Redbreast" class composite gunboat, 6-4inch, 2-3 pdr, built Sheerness Dockyard 1889, 805 tons displacement, 165' long, 31'6" beam, 720 i.h.p., complement 76. The *Goldfinch* became a survey vessel in 1902 and was sold in 1907.

Under the command of F.C. Learmonth the *Goldfinch* replaced the *Stork* in the Mediterranean, but in 1903, her second year of surveying, she was sent to west Africa where she made observations of the Guinea current before crossing the Atlantic taking a line of soundings between Sierra Leone and Bermuda. During 1904 and the early part of 1905 the vessel worked both in the Mediterranean and off the west African coast, suffering many cases of malaria, including Learmonth.

In August 1905 Learmonth was succeeded by F.H. Walter who remained in command until the vessel returned to Sheerness in 1906. Here she was found to be beyond repair and was paid off after only four years of surveying service.

H.M.S. Goldfinch. *Reproduced by permission of the Hydrographer to the Navy.*

During September 1905 she had worked a series of four stations in the neighbourhood of the westerly of the two shoal areas in the Strait of Gibraltar, at about 6°W. Sub-surface current measurements were made with a Pillsbury current meter while surface currents were measured with a drogue. The results gave definite evidence of the sub-surface outflowing current but they were not published until de Buen (1927) maintained that no such outflow existed. In the controversy surrounding de Buen's paper, R. Adm. H.P. Douglas, who had been the Senior Assistant Surveyor on the *Goldfinch* in 1905, published the results as a contribution to the evidence against du Buen's thesis.

References:
de Buen, 1927; Douglas, 1929.

Fisheries Research Vessel Goldseeker. *Courtesy Dept. of Agriculture and Fisheries for Scotland, Aberdeen.*

GOLDSEEKER

Steam trawler built 1900, 206 tons gross, 116′ long, 21′ beam.

Following the establishment of the International Council for the Exploration of the Sea in 1902 the Fishery Board for Scotland undertook the northern half of the British contribution to the proposed international investigations. The programme included biological and hydrographical observations in the northern North Sea and in the Faröe-Shetland Channel and clearly required a more suitable vessel than the tiny *Garland* which had been operated by the Board since 1886. A vessel was also required for the British southern commitment to the investigations, to be undertaken by the Marine Biological Association, and the Government allotted £4,000 for the purchase of the two ships.

D'Arcy W. Thompson was entrusted with acquiring the Fishery Board vessel and eventually obtained the *Goldseeker* in Grimsby, on a sort of hire purchase arrangement, for £1,200 a year for three years with the option of outright purchase for £2,000 at the end of this period.

The *Goldseeker* made numerous cruises up to the outbreak of the First World War, but from 1914 to 1919 she was hired by the Admiralty for examination service.

After the war it was clear that a larger vessel was required, more suitable for deep sea work, and the *Goldseeker* was disposed of in 1922 and replaced by the *Explorer*.

References:
International Council for the Exploration of the Sea, 1928; Thompson, 1958.

HMS GORGON

Wooden paddle frigate, 2-10inch, 4-32 pdr, built Pembroke Dock 1837, 1111 (bm), 178′ long, 37′6″ beam, 320 n.h.p. The *Gorgon* was the first steam vessel in the Royal Navy with a

H.M.S. Gorgon *lying in Homoaze, Plymouth. Artist O.W. Brierly. Courtesy National Maritime Museum. Neg. no. 872.*

tonnage greater than 1000 (bm) and was the first of what became known as paddle frigates, though she was never designated as such herself (see Osbon, 1981). Originally her engines were to have been 220 n.h.p. ones supplied by Boulton and Watt. However, these smaller engines were fitted eventually in the *Hydra,* to be replaced in the *Gorgon* by larger engines made by Seawards of Millwall.

The vessel was employed under the command of Commander Joseph Dayman in 1858 to obtain a line of soundings from Newfoundland to the Azores and thence to England. For most of the soundings Dayman used a relatively thin line with a weight permanently attached, and not detachable as on his sounding voyage in the *Cyclops* in 1857. Consequently, during the *Gorgon* cruise the sounding line generally parted during hauling and sediment samples were obtained from only two casts.

The *Gorgon* was broken up in 1864.

References:
Buchanan and Doughty, 1978; Dayman, 1859; Laing, 1980; Osbon, 1981.

GRANUAILE

Irish Congested Districts Board steamer built by the Ailsa Shipping Company, Troon, 1895, 383 tons gross, 150′ long, 24′ beam, 75 registered h.p.

The *Granuaile* was chartered to the Royal Irish Academy for an expedition to Rockall in 1896 under the leadership of the Rev. W. Spotswood Green. The objective of landing on Rockall was not achieved because of bad weather, but a number of dredge and trawl hauls were made around the islet and on the adjacent banks.

Granuaile is the anglicized version of the Irish name of Grace O'Malley, a 16th century privateer who operated out of Clew Bay, County Mayo.

References:
de Courcy Ireland, 1981 and pers. comm.; Praeger, 1937; Went, 1972.

HMS GRIPER

"Confounder" class gun brig, 2-6 pdr, 10-18 pdr carronades, built by Richards and Co., Hythe 1813, 179 (bm), 84' long, 22' beam.

Under the command of Lieut. M. Liddon the *Griper* accompanied the *Hecla* on W.E. Parry's Arctic voyage of 1819-1820.

Parry was not impressed by the *Griper's* small size and poor sailing qualities and persuaded the Admiralty to replace her by a second bomb vessel on his subsequent Arctic voyages (see *Fury*).

Between May and December 1823 the *Griper* sailed to East Greenland under the command of Cdr. D.C. Clavering (see also *Pheasant*) and with Edward Sabine aboard. Sabine was to carry out pendulum observations in high latitudes to compliment the similar observations he had made off the west coast of Africa in 1822 in the *Pheasant*. Like Parry, Clavering thought the *Griper* was a dreadful vessel.

In 1824 G.F. Lyon (who had command of the *Hecla* during Parry's second Arctic voyage of 1821-23 when Parry himself took command of the *Fury*) was given command of the *Griper* for an unsuccessful voyage in search of a second strait out of Hudson Bay.

The *Griper* became a coastguard vessel in 1825, a target in 1865 and was finally broken up in 1868.

References:
Jones, 1976; Parry, A. 1963; Parry, W.E. 1821.

H.M.S. H.32. Courtesy National Maritime Museum. Neg. no. N 3440.

HMS H32

"H" class submarine, built Vickers 1918, 440 tons displacement, 164'6" long, 16' beam.
Used for physical oceanographic observations in the Bosphorus in 1922 under the command of G.A. Garnons-Williams, in conjunction with H.M.S. *Rocket*.

Reference:
Deacon, 1984.

HARLEQUIN

Steam fishing vessel, built 1885 and originally named the *Shannon,* 139 tons gross, 100′ long, 20′ beam with 70 n.h.p. engines. Hired by the Royal Dublin Society in 1891 to continue a survey of fishing grounds off the Irish coast begun in the *Fingal* in 1890. In addition to a steam windlass and trawling winch, the vessel was fitted with electric lighting supplied by accumulators charged by a dynamo.

Like the *Fingal* survey, the expedition was under the leadership of the Rev. W.S. Green, who also acted as skipper and collected the *Harlequin* in Southampton on 12 March 1891 and returned her in mid-April. Prof. A.C. Haddon, who had been the naturalist on the *Fingal,* was unable to participate in the *Harlequin* cruise and his place was taken by E.W.L. Holt who joined the vessel at Cobh together with his assistant D.H. Lane and C.H.T. Beamish who was to deal with the temperature and specific gravity observations. The vessel sailed around Ireland via the south and west coasts, calling at a number of ports and working a total of 118 stations, mainly using a 48′ beam trawl instead of the much smaller 25′ trawl used for most of the hauls made from the *Fingal.* Most of the hauls were obtained in relatively shallow water but, as with the *Fingal* expedition, one haul was obtained in 900m.

After the *Harlequin* voyage, responsibility for surveying the Irish fishing grounds seems to have passed to the Congested Districts Board, set up in 1891 to help ameliorate the living conditions of the inhabitants of some of the poorest regions of the western coasts of Ireland. To this end, the Board was to encourage a variety of industries, including fishing, and ultimately acquired its own vessel, the *Granuaile.*

The Royal Dublin Society re-entered the field of fisheries research in 1898 with a project to establish a marine laboratory. This laboratory was set up in a Galway brigantine, the *Saturn* (220 gross tons), purchased in 1899 and stationed at Ballynakill Harbour, Co. Galway under the direction of E.W.L. Holt. The laboratory was taken over in 1900 by the newly formed Fishery Branch of the Department of Agriculture and Technical Instruction and eventually replaced, in 1904, by a shore laboratory at Ardfry, Co. Galway.

Also in 1900, the Department acquired the fishery protection vessel *Helga* I and began a long series of exploring cruises around the coasts of Ireland.

References:

References:
Department of Agriculture and Technical Instruction for Ireland, 1902; Holt, 1892; de Courcy Ireland, 1981; Went 1972.

HMS HECLA

"Hecla" class bomb vessel (see also under *Fury*), 2 mortars, 2-6 pdr, 8-24 pdr carronades, built by Barkworth and Hawks, North Barton, 1815, 372 (bm), 105′ long, 28′6″ beam, design complement 67.

Along with the *Fury,* with which she was to be associated later in an exploratory role, the *Hecla* took part in the bombardment of Algiers in 1816. After her return from the Mediterranean she was selected for an expedition together with the *Griper* in search of a North-West Passage to follow up the controversial 1818 voyage of John Ross in the *Isabella* and *Alexander.*

Command of the *Hecla,* and of the expedition, was given to W.E. Parry, who had been Ross's second-in-command. Many of the 1818 expedition members also participated in this second voyage, including James Clark Ross among the midshipmen, and Edward Sabine who once again sailed as astronomer.

From an exploratory point of view the voyage was an enormous success.   Parry left England in May 1819, sailing through Baffin Bay and into Lancaster Sound.   The two ships sailed through Ross's "Croker Mountains" and, after a short digression into Prince Regent Inlet, proceeded westward to Melville Island attaining a longitude of almost 113°W.   Here they wintered, remaining locked in the ice until August 1820, after which Parry returned to England, arriving home in November.

Parry's oceanographic contribution was much less impressive.   He had been given the same instructions as those given to Ross and had most of the same scientific equipment, including Ross's "deep sea clamms".   Parry also had an improved version of Marcet's water sampler, with which Ross had been furnished, the new instrument being closed by the action of "messenger" weights dropped down the line from the surface; according to Deacon (1971, p. 230) this was probably the first use of a technique which is still widely used today.

Although Parry made regular measurements of the surface temperature and specific gravity, he made relatively few sub-surface temperature observations or deep soundings.   He was justifiably critical of the reliability of the self-registering thermometers with which he had been provided and of his ability to obtain accurate soundings, realising that "the weight of the line causes it to run out with a velocity not perceptibly diminished, long after the lead or the clamms have struck the ground".   Accordingly, he was unwilling to devote the necessary time and effort to the extensive use of such unreliable techniques and oceanography was not pursued with any vigour during his later voyages.

Following the geographical success of this first expedition, a new voyage was quickly planned.   The *Hecla* was to be used once more, but the unsatisfactory *Griper* was replaced by the *Fury,* a bomb vessel almost identical to the *Hecla.*   Parry this time took command of the *Fury* and command of the *Hecla* was given to Lieut. G.F. Lyon.   Many of Parry's old officers and men joined him once again, but Sabine's place as astronomer was taken by the Rev. George Fisher who had been with Buchan in the *Dorothea* in 1818.   Having just been ordained, Fisher also acted as the Chaplain to the expedition.   Sabine, in the meantime, was to make pendulum observations off the West African coast from H.M.S. *Pheasant* under the command of D.C. Clavering during 1822 and off East Greenland from the *Griper,* again under Clavering, in 1823.

Compared with the previous voyage, Parry's second arctic voyage was not a great success.   This time he was to proceed to Repulse Bay via Hudson Strait and to continue the search for the north-west passage from this point.   Having left England in May 1821, Parry was unable to find a passage to the west from Repulse Bay and eventually wintered at Winter Island to the south-east of the Melville Peninsula.   During the summer of 1822 the ships moved north, along the eastern coast of the Peninsula, but were unable to penetrate the ice in Fury and Hecla Strait between the Melville Peninsula and Baffin Island.   Parry hoped that the ice conditions were unusually severe and wintered at the entrance to the Strait awaiting better conditions the following summer.   The ice was just as fast in 1823 and Parry abandoned his attempt to find a way through, returning home in October.   Extensive meteorological, astronomical, gravity and magnetic observations had been made during the expedition and a considerable natural history collection was obtained, particularly by James Clark Ross.   However, very little oceanographic work was carried out.

Having demonstrated that there was no hope of finding the sought for northwest passage from Hudson Strait, Parry now undertook his third arctic voyage, this time heading for Prince Regent Inlet as on the 1819 expedition.   The ships selected were once more the *Hecla* and *Fury,* Parry returning to the command of the *Hecla* while Henry Hoppner took the *Fury.*   This voyage was even less successful than the second, for having left England in May 1824 Parry wintered in Prince Regent Inlet, but had to return home in 1825 after abandoning the *Fury* on the shores of Somerset Island.

In 1827 Parry was again in command of the *Hecla,* with James Clark Ross his second-in-command, this time for an attempt to reach the North Pole from Spitsbergen. Parry's plan was to use small boats fitted with runners like sledges to travel over the flat ice reported from the area, an idea put forward by Franklin after the return of the 1818 expedition of the *Dorothea* and *Trent.*

The *Hecla* left England in March and sailed to Spitsbergen in the company of a group of whalers which she had joined in Norway. Having separated from the whalers and having had considerable difficulty with the ice conditions on the Spitsbergen coast, Parry eventually found a safe anchorage for the ship at what became known as *Hecla* Cove in Sorgfjord. Here she was left in the charge of Henry Foster while Parry and Ross took the small boats north, leaving the *Hecla* on 21 June. After covering the first 100 miles or so afloat, the two boats, named *Enterprise* and *Investigator,* took to the ice, but progress over it was much more difficult than Parry had anticipated, made worse by the southerly drift of the ice itself under the influence of the trans-polar current which Nansen made use of in the *Fram* 70 years later. Finally, on 21 July 1827, at 82°45′N, Parry abandoned the attempt and turned south, having achieved a latitude which was not surpassed until the British Arctic Expedition in the *Alert* in 1875-76.

The boats reached open water on August 11, after 48 days on the ice, and arrived at the *Hecla* on the 21st. Foster was away on a surveying expedition but returned a few days later and the *Hecla* left her anchorage on August 28 reaching home in October.

Having been employed in arctic exploration for eight years the *Hecla* remained in surveying for the remainder of her naval service, but with a major climatic change. In December 1827 she was commissioned by Cdr. Thomas Boteler for surveys off the west coast of Africa which lasted until 1830 and was sold in 1831.

References:

Deacon, 1971; Dodge, 1973; Parry, A. 1963; Parry, W.E., 1821, 1824, 1826, 1828.

Helga *(1900). Reproduced from de Courcy Ireland (1981).*

HELGA

Steel twin screw steam yacht, built 1891 by S. M'Knight and Co., Ayr, 283 tons gross, 145′6″ long, 23′ beam, 80 reg. h.p.

The *Helga* was acquired in 1900 by the Fisheries Branch of the Department of Agriculture and Technical Instruction for Ireland under the direction of E.W.L. Holt. The ship was primarily a fisheries protection vessel, but when not engaged in these duties undertook a series of cruises around the Irish coasts including the acquisition of hydrographic data, and mid-water and benthic samples down to depths of some hundreds of metres.

She was replaced in 1908 by a slightly larger vessel given the same name.

References:
Farran, 1928; Le Danois, 1948.

HELGA II

Steel twin screw steam yacht, built 1908 by the Dublin Dockyard Co., 323 tons gross, 111.5 tons net, 155' long, 24'6" beam, 140 n.h.p., 1000 i.h.p. triple expansion engines by David Rowan and Co., Glasgow.

This vessel replaced the earlier *Helga* and continued her fishery protection and surveying duties until the outbreak of the First World War. She had been specially designed for these purposes and was fitted with a trawling winch, deep sea sounding machine and a Hotchkiss three-pounder quick-firing gun.

Between 1901 and 1914 the two *Helgas* worked more than 2000 stations around the coasts of Ireland, making hauls down to depths of about 1600m. The results were published mainly in numerous papers in the *Scientific Investigations* of the Fisheries Branch of the Department of Agriculture and Technical Instruction.

In 1915 the *Helga II* was first hired and later purchased by the Royal Navy as an auxiliary patrol vessel and was used against the Irish nationalists in the Easter Rising in Dublin in 1914.

On the formation of the Irish Free State the ship was sold to the Irish Government and was renamed the *Muirchu,* meaning "Hound of the Sea".

References:
Collins, 1985; de Courcy Ireland, 1981; Green, 1908-09; Morris, 1968.

HMS HERALD

"Atholl" class 6th rate 28, built at the Honourable East India Company yard at Cochin 1822, 500 (bm), 114' long, 32' beam, originally launched as the *Termagant* and renamed in 1824.

During the 1820s and 1830s the *Herald* was employed in general service in the Atlantic, Mediterranean and Indo-Pacific, carrying the Bishops of Barbados and Jamaica to their respective sees and being present at the proclamation of the accession of New Zealand to the Empire in 1840.

In 1845 the *Herald* was converted to a survey ship and was assigned to work on the Pacific coast of north and south America under Capt. Henry Kellett in company with the *Pandora*. Biological collections made by Kellett in the *Herald* and Lieut. James Wood in the *Pandora* were presented to the British Museum, the molluscs having been described by Edward Forbes. The *Herald* had originally carried T. Edmundson as naturalist but he was accidentally shot in 1846 and was replaced by Berthold Seemann who eventually wrote the narrative of the voyage. During this period the *Herald* was diverted to the Arctic from 1848 to 1851 to search for Sir John Franklin's expedition in the *Erebus* and *Terror*.

In 1852 the *Herald* was commissioned by Capt. Henry Denham and surveyed in the south-western Pacific until 1860. On the outward passage Denham met Lieut. I.P. Parker in the U.S.S. *Congress* in Rio. Parker had adopted the then relatively new sounding technique of

H.M.S. Herald *with the paddle gunvessel* Torch. *Illustrated London News. Courtesy National Maritime Museum. Neg. no. 57/1285.*

using a fairly small weight and a thin line and he presented Denham with 15000 fathoms (27435m) of this line. Before the technique was discredited some startling soundings were obtained with it and Denham made one such sounding of 7706 fathoms (14094m) in the South Atlantic!

In 1861 the *Herald* became the chapel ship at Shoreham but was sold for breaking up in 1862.

References:

Dawson, 1885; Day, 1967; Deacon, 1971; Ritchie, 1967; Seemann, 1853; Smith, 1906.

HUXLEY

Steam trawler built 1899, 115' long, 191 tons gross, purchased by G.P. Bidder and hired to the Marine Biological Association for a period of three years from 1902. The *Huxley*, previously the S.S. *Khedive,* was acquired by the M.B.A. in order to fulfill the southern section of the British obligation to the International Fishery Investigations, established following the first meeting of the International Council for the Exploration of the Sea in Copenhagen in 1902 (see also *Goldseeker*).

The *Huxley* was based at the Association's North Sea laboratory established at Lowestoft under the direction of Walter Garstang. The vessel was eventually purchased by the Association and worked extensively in the North Sea and in the Channel until the First World War. From 1915 to 1919 she was hired by the Admiralty and used as a minesweeper. She

Research trawler Huxley. *Courtesy Marine Biological Association, Plymouth.*

was replaced by the *George Bligh* which was purchased in 1920 for the newly opened MAFF laboratory founded at Lowestoft to succeed the MBA laboratory.

The vessel was sold in 1910 to W. Crampin for £2,400.

References:
Allen, 1904-06; ICES, 1928.

HMS HYDRA

Wooden paddle sloop, built Chatham Dockyard 1838, 818 (bm), 165′ long, 33′ beam, 220 n.h.p. engines built by Boulton and Watt (see also under *Gorgon*).

Hydra was employed in obtaining soundings in the Mediterranean, off the east coast of Sicily, during 1867 under the command of Capt. P.F. Shortland. Shortland was ordered to proceed to Bombay and to carry out a sounding survey from Bombay to Kuria Muria and thence to Aden for a proposed submarine cable. The series of soundings in the Indian Ocean and a number in the Atlantic during the return voyage to England were conducted during 1868 using a modification of Brooke's sounding apparatus devised during the voyage. The *Hydra* sounder, incorporating a spring to throw off the line supporting the detachable weights, was widely used by Royal Naval vessels in the next few years, including the *Challenger,* until it was superseded by the Baillie sounder in 1873.

Shortland also measured deep temperatures and must have been using thermometers protected against pressure since, apparently, he recorded 33° to 34°F from depths over 2000 fathoms (3640m). Shortland's temperature measurements were sent to the Admiralty in 1868 and were clearly at variance with the belief, still widely held at the time, that the great depths of the sea had a constant temperature of about 39°F (see also under *Isabella*). W.B. Carpenter learned of these low temperature measurements, and of the different temperature-density characteristics of fresh and salt water, shortly before the *Lightning* sailed and was therefore prepared for the deep temperatures recorded during the voyage which finally dispelled the 39°F theory.

References:

Buchanan and Doughty, 1978; Deacon, 1971, 1978; McConnell, 1982; Shortland, 1869

HMS INVESTIGATOR

Ship sloop, 6-12 pdr, 2-18 pdr, 2 swivel, 344 tons (bm), 100'4" long, 28'5" beam, purchased 1798 as an armed vessel. Originally named *Xenophon*, the vessel was renamed *Investigator* for Matthew Flinders' exploration of the Australian coast in 1801 to 1803, the first naval vessel to carry this name.

Flinders sailed along the south, east and north coasts of the continent from Cape Leeuwin to Cape Wilberforce, calling at Port Jackson (later Sydney) where he met with the French vessels *Le Géographe* and *Le Naturaliste* in the course of a circumnavigation under Nicolas Baudin and with François Péron as naturalist.

During the survey of the Gulf of Carpentaria, Flinders discovered that many of the ship's timbers were rotten so that she was in danger of breaking up if she were driven ashore. After a short visit to Cupang on the island of Timor, he took the *Investigator* back to Port Jackson, completing the circumnavigation of Australia but remaining offshore to avoid unnecessary dangers. At Port Jackson Flinders transferred first to the *Porpoise*, which was lost on a reef, and then to the *Cumberland* for the passage home to England. The tragic story of his journey, including six and half years as a prisoner of the French on Ile de France (Mauritius) is one of the saddest episodes in the history of British naval exploration. Flinders finally reached England in 1810 as the old *Investigator*, which herself had been brought back with some difficulty in 1805, was being broken up at Plymouth.

Apart from surveying and exploration, the objectives of the original voyage had a considerable scientific content, particularly in botanical collections, and for this purpose Flinders had taken with him Robert Brown, Sir Joseph Banks' botanist librarian, Ferdinand Bauer, a botanical draughtsman, and Peter Good, an accomplished gardener. The resulting enormous collection of Australian plants was by far the most important collection brought back, but minerals and shells were also collected.

Flinders' oceanographic observations were very limited, but he recorded the surface temperature daily for the first six weeks of the voyage, and he also measured the temperature once at 150 fathoms (274m) and once at 200 fathoms (365m) using a "bucket" with which he had been supplied to obtain sub-surface water samples.

References:

Deacon, 1971; Flinders 1814; Ritchie, 1967; Stearn, 1981.

RIMS INVESTIGATOR

Royal Indian Marine wooden paddle steamer, built Bombay 1881, 580 tons (Alcock), 856 tons (Colledge), 180' long, 26' beam.

After the abolition of the Indian Navy in 1862, surveys in Indian waters almost came to a halt

R.I.M.S. Investigator *(1881). Courtesy National Maritime Museum. Neg. no. 59/1072.*

R.I.M.S. Investigator *(1881). Agassiz trawl being lowered. Courtesy National Maritime Museum. Neg. no. 59/1074.*

until the establishment of the Indian Marine Survey under Cdr. A. Dundas Taylor in 1874. The main function of the Survey was to work in relatively shallow waters for the purposes of navigation. However, on the recommendation of the Asiatic Society of Bengal, and with the support of Dundas Taylor, it was agreed that deep sea dredging should be carried out wherever possible and the post of surgeon-naturalist was therefore established from the inception of the Survey (see under *Clyde*).

Initially, the Survey had no suitable vessel for this work and the post of surgeon-naturalist lapsed from 1879 to 1884. Consequently, for the first two years of her operations the *Investigator* had no naturalist aboard and carried out no deep dredging, though some deep sea soundings were taken.

In 1884 Cdr. Alfred Carpenter, who had served in the *Challenger* during the latter part of her oceanographic voyage, was given command of the Survey, and G.M.J. Giles was appointed surgeon-naturalist. Deep dredging now began seriously, initially using hemp rope and a dredge similar to that used on the *Challenger,* but subsequently wire rope and a reversible Agassiz trawl. In both cases the warp was led over the bows and the dredge was towed with the vessel going astern, a technique which seems to have been quite widespread at the time and was certainly adopted on the *Porcupine* and *Valorous.* Opportunities for obtaining deep hauls were limited to the *Investigator's* passages between the shallow-water survey areas. In the early years these surveys were carried out in Indian and Burmese coastal waters, with frequent passages between these regions so that there were ample opportunities for dredging in the Bay of Bengal. From about 1904 the whole of the surveying season was spent in one region, so that opportunities for deep dredging were restricted to the passages at the beginning and end of each season. As a consequence, the number of samples obtained each year decreased. Nevertheless, by the time the vessel was replaced by the new *Investigator* in 1908, more than 200 deep dredge hauls had been made in depths down to almost 2000 fathoms (3640m) by a succession of surgeon-naturalists including A.W. Alcock and A.R.S. Anderson, the former ultimately becoming Superintendent of the Indian Museum.

In 1890 a draughtsman was appointed to illustrate the material collected, and from 1892 a series of plates were produced to illustrate the *Investigator* Memoirs published by the Indian Museum between 1889 and 1914.

In addition to the biological work, extensive sounding and temperature measurements were made, the near bottom and surface temperatures being measured routinely with each dredging operation, and deep sea sediment samples collected. Some of these results were published at the time (see Carpenter, 1887 and Oldham, 1895) but many were collated much later by R.B. Seymour Sewell, surgeon-naturalist of the Survey from 1910 to 1925.

References:
Alcock, 1898, 1901; Sewell, 1925, 1935, 1952.

RIMS INVESTIGATOR

Royal Indian Marine Survey vessel, built Vickers and Maxim, 1907, 1018 tons gross, 254' long, 33' beam.

This vessel replaced the old *Investigator* from 1908 onwards and, with the exception of the years of the First World War, carried on the surveying work in Indian waters until she was sold in 1934. For most of this time, from 1910 to 1925, the surgeon-naturalist was R.B. Seymour Sewell who went on to become Director of the Zoological Survey of India and, in 1933-34, the scientific leader of the John Murray / Mabahiss Expedition.

R.I.M.S. Investigator *(1907). Courtesy National Maritime Museum. Neg. no. A 8167.*

The reduction in the opportunities for deep-sea work during the last few years of operation of the old *Investigator* continued after the new vessel came into service, so that between 1910 and 1925 only 13 deep trawl or dredge hauls were made according to Sewell (1952), compared with 128 during the first fifteen years of the Survey's deep sea work. In place of the dredging work, Sewell made extensive surface plankton collections and a limited number in mid-water, concentrating his studies on the copepods and making major contributions to the knowledge of both the taxonomy and zoogeography of this group in the Indian Ocean.

When Sewell left the Survey in 1925 the post of surgeon-naturalist was held for one year by R.W.G. Hingston, but was not filled after his resignation. Consequently, the biological work of the surgeon-naturalist, carried out almost continuously since 1884, ceased in 1926.

Reference:
Sewell, 1952.

ISABELLA

Brig of 383 (bm), 110′ long, 28′ beam, hired by the Admiralty for the first of many naval expeditions to polar regions in the nineteenth century.

In 1817 William Scoresby Jnr brought back the news that the waters around Greenland were unusually free from ice. Sir Joseph Banks, President of the Royal Society, wrote to Lord Melville, the First Lord of the Admiralty, suggesting that a naval expedition should be despatched in search of the North-West Passage between the Atlantic and Pacific. John Barrow, the Second Secretary to the Admiralty, accepted this suggestion enthusiastically since he was anxious to redirect the resources of the Navy after the disastrous West African venture in the *Congo* in 1815 (q.v.). Accordingly, a two pronged attack was planned, a western expedition in the *Isabella* and *Alexander* to seek a passage from Baffin Bay, and an eastern expedition in the *Dorothea* and *Trent* to look for the expected open polar sea north of Spitsbergen.

Command of the *Isabella* (complement 57) and of the western expedition was given to Cdr. John Ross, with Lieut. William Edward Parry in command of the *Alexander* (complement 37). Ross was accompanied on the *Isabella* by his 18-year old midshipman nephew James Clark Ross who, like Parry, was destined to become a much more famous polar explorer than his uncle, and by Captain Edward Sabine of the Royal Artillery who sailed as supernumerary on the recommendation of the Royal Society. Sabine was to assist Ross "in making such observations as may trend to the improvement of geography and navigation, and the advancement of science in general." For although the primary aim of the voyage was geographical, Ross was instructed to make a wide variety of observations on magnetism, meteorology, tides, currents and soundings, and to collect biological, mineralogical and seabed samples. Ross assiduously followed these instructions and, although the voyage lasted only from April to November, it was more productive scientifically than any other naval expedition during the next decade. Unfortunately, this aspect of the voyage was overshadowed by a controversy over Ross's claim that Lancaster Sound was blocked by a non-existent range of mountains through which Parry sailed in the *Hecla* and *Griper* in 1819.

Prior to the voyage, the deepest reliable sounding is generally considered to be that of Phipps in H.M.S. *Racehorse* in 683 fathoms (1250m) to the east of Iceland in 1773. Ross reported over 100 soundings in Baffin's Bay, including four between 1000 and 1070 fathoms (1830-1957m), one of which brought up a large bottom living starfish. These soundings were accepted uncritically by Wyville Thomson and Carpenter in the 1860s when Ross was credited with having provided the first demonstration of the existence of life at such depths. The depths of these soundings were probably overestimated by a factor of at least two (see Rice, 1975). However, even if such an error had been recognised at the time, the "starfish" sounding should have provided strong evidence against Edward Forbes' azoic theory, based

The Isabella *and* Alexander *moored to the ice at Prince Regent's Inlet while Ross and Parry meet the natives. Reproduced from* Ross, *1819.*

largely on his *Beacon* dredgings, which so dominated marine biology until the cruises of the *Lightning* and *Porcupine.*

Similarly, Ross's sub-surface temperature measurements, using Six's self-registering thermometers (see McConnell, 1982), were of great potential significance. First, Ross made temperature measurements at a series of different depths, a practice which was later to provide the basic data for physical oceanographers. More importantly, however, he recorded consistently decreasing temperatures with increasing depths, down to 25.5°F in one case. Ross was able to corroborate his *in situ* thermometer results by measuring the temperature of bottom mud brought to the surface in the "deep-sea clamms" which were made by the ship's armourer during the cruise. The clamms consisted of a pair of jaws which closed together around a sediment sample when the instrument struck bottom.

Alexander Marcet, who examined Ross's temperature results and the water samples brought back, realised that salt water becomes heavier with decreasing temperature until it freezes, unlike freshwater which has a maximum density at about 39°F (4°C). Marcet's conclusions and Ross's temperature measurements were largely disregarded and the so-called "4° theory", according to which the great ocean depths were filled with a heavy mass of water at this temperature, was widely adopted during the 1840s and 1850s until, like the azoic theory, it was finally dispelled by the results obtained from the *Lightning* and *Porcupine.*

Following the 1818 voyage the *Isabella* reverted to her whaling role and, by a remarkable coincidence, fifteen years later rescued John Ross's second arctic expedition. As a result of the controversy caused by the 1818 voyage Ross was unable to obtain a further naval command. His second voyage was therefore financed largely by the gin manufacturer Felix Booth, though he was accompanied by several of the naval officers of his earlier expedition, including James Clark Ross, by then a Commander, who sailed as second-in-command. After leaving England in May 1829 the steam vessel *Victory* sailed through Lancaster Sound into Prince Regent Inlet and collected stores from the wreck site of the *Fury* (q.v.) on the shores of Somerset Island. Ross sailed south during the late summer of 1829 and established winter quarters at Lord Mayor Bay. During each of the succeeding two summers the *Victory* could be moved only a few miles before she again became locked in the ice, and early in 1832 Ross decided to abandon her and attempt an escape by sledge and boat. The winter of 1832 / 33 was spent at Fury Beach and Ross was eventually able to take to the boats in August 1833. After sailing north into Lancaster Sound and then east, beyond Navy Board Inlet, on 26 August Ross encountered a whaler which turned out to be the *Isabella*. Since Ross's party had already been in the Arctic for more than four years, a record which still stands, and had been given up for lost two years previously in England, it is difficult to know whether Ross or the *Isabella's* captain, John Humphreys was the more surprised! The Expedition did not carry out any significant oceanographic work, but its main scientific achievement was the determination of the position of the North Magnetic Pole by James Clark Ross.

References:

Deacon, 1971; Dodge, 1973; Jones, 1972a; McConnell, 1982; Marcet, 1819; Rice, 1975; Ross, 1819, 1835.

ISABELLA

Tender to the *Beacon* in the Mediterranean from 1841 until 1846 when she was replaced by the *Research.* See under *Beacon.*

Reference:

Deacon, 1978.

HMS JACKAL

Twin screw iron fishery protection vessel, 750 tons displacement, 148′ long, 26′ beam, 814 i.h.p., purchased in 1885 as the tug *Woodcock* and renamed in 1886.

In 1887 the *Jackal* was used, under the command of Lieut. A.M. Farquhar, for a physical and chemical cruise to the Hebrides for the Scottish Fisheries Board with Hugh Robert Mill as scientist. Mill was on the staff of the Scottish Marine Station, originally established on a floating laboratory, the *Ark,* at Granton in the Firth of Forth in 1884. The Marine Station was financed by the Scottish Meteorological Society and its establishment had been recommended by the Society's fisheries committee of which John Murray was chairman. Mill was given leave of absence to take part in the Fisheries Board cruise because the original choice, John Gibson, disliked working at sea. Mill suggested that the only significant result of this cruise was his coining of the term Continental Shelf!

In 1893-1894 the *Jackal* was used for a further series of similar cruises to investigate the water masses flowing through the channels connecting the North Sea with the Norwegian Sea and the Atlantic, including the Faröe-Shetland Channel, this time with H.N. Dickson as the scientist. These cruises had the twin objectives of extending the observations made by Mill and also being the British contribution to the international survey of the North Sea and North Atlantic proposed by Scandinavian scientists, particularly Otto Pettersson and Gustaf Ekman.

Like so many other survey vessels, the *Jackal* seems to have been particularly unsuitable for the work for which she was used, for she could not steam at less than about 4 knots and she could not be hove to. Nevertheless, extensive sounding, submarine temperature and salinity observations were made down to depths of about 400 fathoms (728m). The sediment samples collected on the sounding leads were examined by John Murray, while the small number of townet samples, obtained at the request of Pettersson, were examined by W.C. McIntosh and A. Scott.

References:

Deacon, 1971; Dickson, 1893; McConnell, 1982; Mill, H.R. 1951.

KNIGHT ERRANT

Paddle steamer built Hull, 1862, 180 tons gross, 127′ long.

The *Knight Errant* was hired by the Admiralty from her owner, George Percival of Liverpool, for survey work off the west coast of Scotland in 1880 under the command of T.H. Tizard who had been the Navigating Lieutenant in the *Challenger.*

During the *Challenger* voyage Tizard had been responsible for the serial temperature measurements and he and Wyville Thomson had discussed some of the *Challenger* results in relation to those obtained in the Faröe-Shetland Channel from the *Lightning* and *Porcupine.* In particular, in the East Indies the *Challenger* scientists had encountered several areas in which the temperature in the lower part of the water column remained constant instead of decreasing regularly from the surface to the bottom as it did in the open sea. They concluded that each of these areas were deep basins cut off from the general oceanic circulation by ridges connecting the islands which surrounded them. There was no opportunity to test the existence of these ridges by sounding from the *Challenger,* but both Thomson and Tizard felt that a similar explanation applied to the "cold" and "warm" areas encountered in the Faröe-Shetland Channel, and after the return of the *Challenger* Thomson was anxious to investigate the area more intensively.

He obtained the support of the Hydrographer, F.J.O. Evans, for a cruise in 1879, but had to postpone it because of ill-health.   When he asked for help again in 1880 he was offered the use of the *Knight Errant,* which was already working in the general area, as long as he provided the equipment necessary for dredging and the ship's surveying work was not seriously interfered with.

A steam winch for dredging was loaned by the firm of D. and W. Henderson and fitted at their Partick works, where the *Knight Errant* was joined by John Murray and Frank Pearcy who had been Thomson's laboratory assistant on the *Challenger.*

The ship sailed to Stornoway via Oban where she was joined by Thomson and his son Frank.   Between 26 July and 14 August the *Knight Errant* made four short cruises to the Faröe-Shetland Channel, returning to Stornoway after each cruise, though Wyville Thomson stayed ashore again because of his poor health and returned to the mainland at the end of the second cruise.

Soundings obtained during the cruises demonstrated the existence of the suspected ridge and limited townet and trawl hauls were made in the cold and warm areas.   However, a combination of bad weather and deficiencies of the ship, and particularly her very limited coal carrying capacity, limited seriously the success of the undertaking.   Consequently, Thomson applied to the Admiralty, through the Royal Society, for a more extensive dredging expedition to the ridge in a more suitable vessel.   This application was turned down, but two years later, and after Thomson's death in March 1882, John Murray was successful in a similar application and had a very fruitful cruise in H.M.S. *Triton,* again under the command of Tizard.

References:
Deacon, 1977; Thomson, 1880; Tizard and Murray, 1882.

HMS L6

"L" class submarine, built Beardmore 1918, 890 tons displacement, 222' long, 23'6" beam.
Following an original proposal by G.H. Fowler, *L6* was equipped for physical oceanographic observations including continuous temperature monitoring, water sampling and current measurement.   The vessel worked in the Bristol Channel during the autumn of 1921 under the command of Lieut. J. Blackburn and with D.J. Matthews aboard as scientist.   The project was abandoned early in 1922.

Reference:
Deacon, 1984.

LALLA ROOKH

Sailing schooner, built at Poole 1854, 82' long, 19' beam, 94 reg. tons, 121 tons Thames Measurement.   Purchased by Sir William Thomson (Lord Kelvin) in 1870.

Thomson spent most of his free time sailing during the 1870s and early 1880s, cruising mainly in British waters but also making a voyage to Gibraltar in 1872 and at least two visits to Madeira, his second wife's home.   Though he worked at his ideas and publications while on board, sailing was clearly a relaxation and he does not seem to have carried out a regular programme of oceanographic researches.   However, he used the opportunity the voyages provided to test new equipment such as sounders and depth gauges, and improvements to them, and many of his scientific enterprises had a nautical element.   Thus, he first used steel pianowire for soundings from the *Lalla Rookh* (but see also *Medea*), and in June 1872, during his

95

Lalla Rookh. *Reproduced from Thompson, 1910.*

Gibraltar voyage, he made a sounding of 2600 fathoms (4758m) in the Bay of Biscay by this technique. During hauling in, the reel on which the wire was stored was under enormous pressure, but despite distortion Thomson retrieved the attached sampler and its sample of sediment.

Later that same year one of Thomson's sounding machines was placed on board the *Challenger,* but its sea trials were not successful and the *Challenger* soundings were subsequently routinely obtained using rope and a donkey engine. The Americans, on the other hand, enthusiastically adopted Thomson's technique and, with some modifications, used it with great success from the USS *Tuscarora* in the Pacific in 1873-74 and later from the Coast Survey vessel USS *Blake.*

In 1871 Thomson's observations with the German scientist Hermann von Helmholtz on the *Lalla Rookh* led them to discuss the theory of waves. According to Laurence Pullar it was while yachting off Skye in 1870 that Thomson met John Murray and was so impressed with his account of marine luminescence that two years later he recommended him for the *Challenger* expedition.

References:
McConnell, 1982; Pullar, 1910; Thompson, S.P. 1910; Thomson, 1873-1875.

HMS LARK

Survey schooner, built Barnstaple 1880, 166 (bm).
From 1881 to 1887 the *Lark* was employed in surveying work in the southwestern Pacific under the command of C.F. Oldham from 1881 to 1884 and T.F. Pullen from 1884 to 1887

H.M.S. Lark. *Reproduced by permission of the Hydrographer to the Navy.*

when she was found to be unseaworthy. The *Lark's* surgeon, H.B. Guppy, carried out a study of the geology and natural history of the Solomon Islands in 1882-84 and the collections were presented to the British Museum.

The *Lark* was sold at Sydney in 1888.

References:
Day, 1967; Deacon, 1972; Guppy, 1882-1885, 1884-1886.

HMS LIGHTNING

Wooden paddle gunvessel, 3 guns, built Deptford 1823, 296 (bm), 126' long, 22'8" beam, 100 n.h.p.

The *Lightning,* along with her sister vessel the *Meteor,* and the later (1827) built *Echo,* were the first steam powered warships to appear in the Navy List which they entered in January 1828. However, these were not the first powered warships to be built for the Royal Navy since this distinction apparently belongs to the *Comet* (built 1822) though this vessel did not appear in the Navy List until 1831.

During her long life the *Lightning* served for several periods as a survey vessel. In 1835 she was used for surveying in the Irish Sea under the command of Edward Belcher who left the vessel to take command of the *Sulphur* after Beechey was invalided home from Valparaiso. In 1854-55 the *Lightning* was sent to assist in the Baltic campaign against Russia, under Capt. B.J. Sulivan, and performed important surveying and pathfinding duties in the waters around Lumpar Island (see frontispiece). In 1865-67 she was commanded by Capt. E.J. Bedford for surveying work on the west coasts of the British Isles, and in 1868 was made available to Charles Wyville Thomson and W.B. Carpenter for a short cruise to the north-west of Scotland which ensured her an important place in the development of oceanography.

Model of H.M.S. Lightning. *Courtesy National Maritime Museum. Neg. no. C5558b.*

In early 1868 Carpenter visited Belfast, where Thomson was Professor of Natural History at Queen's College, to continue their collaboration on the sea lilies or crinoids. The previous year Thomson had visited Michael Sars in Norway and had seen a variety of organisms dredged by Sars' son, George Ossian, from depths down to 450 fathoms (823m) near the Lofoten Islands, including a crinoid which resembled closely a form otherwise known only as a fossil.

Over the previous 40 years, evidence against Edward Forbes' azoic theory (see *Beacon*) had been accumulating gradually. This included John Ross's retrieval of a starfish on a deep sounding line on the *Isabella* in 1818, largely ignored at the time, Wallich's similar experience on the *Bulldog* in 1860, James Clark Ross's dredgings from the *Erebus* and *Terror,* and particularly, thought Thomson, the discovery of animals attached to the Sardinia to Bona telegraph cable brought up for repair from 1200 fathoms (2184m) in 1860. These results, and Sars' dredgings, suggested that the deep sea might contain a previously unsuspected rich fauna, and that this might include forms of great phylogenetic interest. Accordingly, Thomson and Carpenter agreed that when the latter returned to London Thomson would write to him in his capacity as a member of the Council of the Royal Society urging the Society to use its influence to encourage the Admiralty to organise a deep dredging expedition. Carpenter passed Thomson's letter, together with his own in support of the suggestion, to the Society's President, Edward Sabine, who had had a long association with marine exploration going back to Ross's 1818 voyage.

The Royal Society approached the Admiralty in June 1868 and on 8 August the *Lightning* sailed from Oban with Thomson, Carpenter and his son P.H. Carpenter on board and under the command of Staff Commander W.H. May. Although the principal objective of the voyage was deep dredging, the Hydrographer, G.H. Richards, took advantage of it to have a variety of deep-sea thermometers tested and compared.

The first part of the cruise was an almost total failure, for a combination of bad weather and the condition of the *Lightning,* already 45 years old and, according to Thomson (1872), virtually falling apart, prevented any deep dredging being accomplished.

After calling at Stornoway on the Isle of Lewis, the vessel sailed north in strong winds and was able to make only a few dredge hauls in 50 to 200 fathoms (90-360m) on the Faröe Bank before sheltering in Thorshavn for a week. On 26 August they left Thorshavn but suffered a further three days of gales, almost losing the mast when several of the rigging fastenings parted.

Finally, on 29th the weather improved sufficiently for the dredge to be fished at a depth of 510 fathoms (933m) about 100 miles south east of Thorshavn (Stn 6, see chart). The catch was small, but several groups were represented, including crustaceans and echinoderms. Bad weather set in again and no further deep dredging was possible until September 3 when a similarly small catch was obtained at a depth of 500 fathoms (910m) (Stn 7).

During the first part of the cruise the near bottom temperatures recorded were consistently between about 7° and 10°C, but since leaving Thorshavn much lower deep temperatures had been encountered, those at stations 6 and 7 being 0.5° and 1.1°C respectively. During the next few days further bad weather prevented dredging, but on a line of soundings to the north-west of station 7 bottom temperatures close to or even below 0°C were recorded consistently.

On September 6 a dramatically different situation was encountered. The *Lightning* had moved some 60 miles to the south of the previous station and here (Stn 12), at a depth of 530 fathoms (969m), a bottom temperature of 6.4°C was found and the dredge retrieved a much richer catch than during the previous hauls, comprised of quite different species and dominated by the glass sponge *Holtenia* (= *Pheronema*) *carpenteri.*

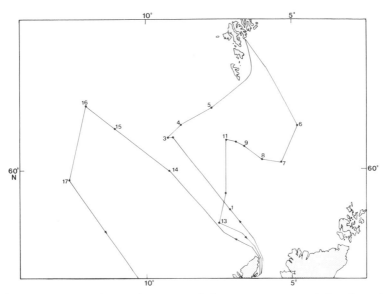

Track of H.M.S. Lightning *in August and September 1868, with the station positions marked. Redrawn from Thomson, 1873, plate I.*

The *Lightning* now made for Stornoway where Thomson had to leave, but Carpenter and his son remained on the vessel for a further short cruise to the north-west of the Hebrides in search of even deeper water than had been encountered previously. After leaving Stornoway on 14 September, soundings were obtained at four localities in depths between 570 and 650 fathoms (1043 and 1189m respectively) and at three of these stations bottom temperatures between 6°

and 7°C were measured.   At the fourth locality (station 16 in 650 fathoms) the sounding lead and thermometers were lost so that no bottom temperature was obtained, but a successful dredge haul was made and a variety of animals were collected.

On 17 September the weather began to deteriorate once more and, with no prospect of improvement, it was decided to terminate the cruise.   Carpenter and his son were landed at Oban and the *Lightning* continued to Pembroke where she docked on 25, but not before almost losing the foremast off the Isle of Man when a hook holding the forerigging parted without warning!

The poor performance of the *Lightning,* the bad weather encountered, and the fact that the deepest dredge haul was in only 650 fathoms, combined to make the results of the cruise somewhat disappointing.   Nevertheless, the existence of abundant and varied life at much greater depths than had been sampled previously by dredge had been demonstrated clearly. Moreover, the near-bottom temperature measurements were clearly contrary to the "4°C theory" (see also under *Isabella* and *Hydra*) which was based on the erroneous belief that salt water, like fresh water, had a maximum density at about 4°C, so that the deeper parts of the ocean were thought to be filled with water at this temperature.   Both Carpenter and Thomson had believed this to be so up to the time of the *Lightning* cruise, but by the time he wrote up the *Lightning* results Carpenter was aware of the error.   Nevertheless, Deacon (1971, p. 329) has pointed out that this myth lived on in some quarters and "appeared in Parliament as recently as 1961 in the mouth of the then Civil Lord of the Admiralty".

Carpenter went on to explain the widely differing near bottom temperatures in localities not widely separated in terms of a general oceanic circulation maintained by density differences caused by such temperature variations.   The existence of the Wyville Thomson Ridge, subsequently surveyed by the *Knight Errant* and *Triton,* was unsuspected at the time and Carpenter suggested that the situation encountered by the *Lightning* was caused by the presence of a warm current moving northwards from the Atlantic and a cold current bringing water from the Arctic.   He was particularly anxious to investigate this phenomenon further in the subsequent voyage which he and Thomson urged the Royal Society to recommend to the Admiralty and which took place the following year in the *Porcupine.*

The *Lightning* spent her last two years in surveying on the west coast of the British Isles under Staff Cdr. J. Richards and was broken up at Devonport in 1872,

References:

Carpenter, 1868-69; Deacon, 1971; Thomson, 1872.

LORD BANDON

Paddle steamer built South Shields by J.T. Eltringham 1878, 122' long, 19' beam, 154 tons gross, twin steam engines developing 95 n.h.p., used for three cruises off the south and west of Ireland in 1885, 1886 and 1888, sponsored by the Royal Irish Academy.

In 1885 the Academy made a grant to E. Perceval Wright, Professor of Zoology at Trinity College, Dublin, to organize a committee to investigate the fauna around the 100 fathom line off the south-west coasts of Ireland.   As a result the *Lord Bandon* was chartered from the Queenstown Towing Company for a cruise from 3-8 August under the leadership of W. Spotswood Green accompanied by the vessel's owner, T.W. Weeks.   A total of 30 hauls were obtained, the deepest at 120 fathoms (220m).

From 5-16 June 1886 Green led a second cruise on the *Lord Bandon,* now owned by the Clyde Shipping Company, Glasgow.   This time 34 hauls were obtained, 9 over 100 fathoms deep, including trawl hauls to 265 fathoms (485m) and dredge hauls to 325 fathoms (595m).

By 1888 the vessel's name had been changed to *Flying Falcon* and she was chartered for 10 days, together with her crew of 10 men, for £60! This time the vessel dredged to a depth of 1270 fathoms (2323m).

Conventional hemp rope was used during the 1885 voyage, but wire rope was employed for both trawling and sounding in the later voyages.

References:
Haddon and Green, 1887; O'Riordan, 1967; Went, 1972.

HEMS MABAHISS

Egyptian fisheries research vessel, built Tyneside 1930, 138′ long, 23′6″ beam, 200 tons deadweight.

The *Mabahiss* (arabic for 'Researches') was originally intended for fisheries research in the Mediterranean and Red Seas, but in 1933-1934 she was used for the John Murray Expedition in the Indian Ocean, financed almost entirely by British, albeit private, funds and staffed mainly by British scientists, thus justifying her inclusion in a book on British oceanographic vessels.

Sir John Murray, who was killed in a car accident in 1914, had left a bequest of 250 shares in the Christmas Island Phosphate Company (see Burstyn, 1975), the dividend from which was to be used for research in oceanography or limnology. By 1931 a considerable sum had accumulated in the bequest and Murray's son, John Challenger Murray, enlisted the help of a number of scientists to organise a major oceanographic expedition. The area chosen was the western Indian Ocean, a region which had not been visited during the *Challenger* Expedition and which had received little attention subsequently.

H.E.M.S. Mabahiss *undergoing trials. Courtesy Swan Hunter Shipbuilders Ltd.*

It was intended originally that the *Mabahiss* would be involved in a subsidiary exploration of the Red Sea while the main expedition was in the Indian Ocean. However, the ships considered for the main expedition, the *William Scoresby*, the *Dana* and the research trawler *George Bligh*, were found to be either unsuitable or unavailable, so that when the Egyptian Government offered the loan of *Mabahiss* it was accepted with alacrity.

The scientific leadership of the Expedition was given to Lt. Col. R.B. Seymour Sewell who had retired recently from a long career in the Indian Medical Service during which he had participated in extensive marine biological work in the Indian Ocean as Surgeon naturalist to the Marine Survey of India (see *Investigator*). Sewell's scientific team consisted of three British scientists, E.F. Thompson, H.C. Gilson and T.T. Macan, and two Egyptians, A.F. Mohamed and H. Faouzi, who also acted as ship's doctor. In addition, Lt. Cdr. W.I. Farquharson was seconded from the Royal Navy to act as second in command and navigator, responsible also for the surveying and sounding work.

Command of the *Mabahiss* was given to K.N. MacKenzie who had sailed on the *Discovery* during the B.A.N.Z.A.R. Expeditions in 1929-1931, initially as Chief Officer and subsequently as Master. Apart from the Chief Engineer and Radio Officer the remaining officers and crew of the *Mabahiss* were all Egyptian.

Mabahiss sailed from Alexandria on 3 September 1933 and returned on 25 May 1934 having sailed about 22000 miles and worked a total of 209 stations in the Red Sea, Gulf of Aden, Indian Ocean and Gulf of Oman. The main objective of the cruise was undoubtedly the collection of benthic biological samples with the trawls and dredges which were used at almost every station, and the relatively small number of plankton samples which were also obtained. The taxonomic accounts of these biological collections filled the bulk of the official expedition reports which were published between 1935 and 1967 by the British Museum (Natural History) where most of the material is housed. The collections were, and are, of considerable importance, particularly since no extensive collections of the deep-sea fauna in the areas visited had previously been made other than those of the Indian Marine Survey vessels *Investigator* I and II between 1885 and 1925. However, the chemical and physical observations were of more general potential importance. Gilson, whose principal responsibility during the cruise was the

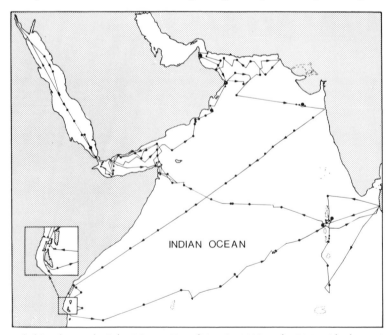

Track of H.E.M.S. Mabahiss *during the John Murray Expedition in 1933 and 1934, with the station positions marked. Redrawn from Sewell, 1935.*

investigation of the relationship between the phytoplankton and nutrients in the water column, made important contributions to an understanding of the nitrogen cycle in the open ocean. Unfortunately, the detailed temperature, salinity and oxygen profiles obtained were never published, so that the significance of the oxygen minimum layer and the more or less azoic areas of sea-floor off the coast of Arabia and in the Gulf of Oman, encountered during the cruise, was not appreciated at the time.

In retrospect, the topographic results were potentially even more important than the hydrographic ones, but the theoretical framework within which to interpret them correctly did not come into existence for a further twenty years. Before the *Mabahiss* sailed, the sea-floor topography of the north-western Indian Ocean was very poorly known. At the end of the cruise Farquharson was able to produce bathymetric charts showing all of the major features of the region, including three which are fundamental to modern ideas of sea-floor spreading and plate tectonics. First, the work in the Gulf of Aden revealed NE-SW trending ridges which are now recognised as transform faults between the African and Arabian plates. Second, a series of gullies and ridges encountered parallel to the Makran coast are now seen to be caused by the folding of sediments as the Arabian Plate slides beneath the Eurasian Plate. Finally, the mid-ocean ridge, crossed by a single echo-sounding run by the *Dana* in 1930 and named the Carlsberg Ridge, was crossed three times by the *Mabahiss,* revealing the presence of an axial valley now known to be typical of divergent plate boundaries. In the 1930s the idea of Continental Drift and of horizontal movements generally were very unfashionable among most geologists. Consequently, these topographical results, and the analyses of basalts dredged from the Carlsberg Ridge which showed them to be quite different from those of the Deccan Trap in India, were at the time interpreted in terms of vertical movements and particularly as arguing against the existence of an ancient land bridge between Africa and India. Their true significance did not become apparent until the development of plate tectonics in the 1960s.

After the John Murray Expedition the *Mabahiss* made a series of short cruises in the Red Sea over the winter of 1934-35 which were to have been in preparation for a much more extensive study of the region. Financial and political factors, including the outbreak of the Second World War, prevented this major expedition ever taking place and *Mabahiss* therefore reverted to fisheries and coast-guard duties in Egyptian coastal waters until 1959. At this time she was transferred to the Egyptian Ports and Lights Administration and was used to supply lighthouses and inspect navigation lights until 1965 when she was laid up in Alexandria with the intention of refitting her for use as a research vessel once more. This work was started, but by 1970 it was clear that insufficient funds were available to complete the refit and all work was stopped. Since that time the ship has lain in Alexandria until 1983 when ownership was transferred to the University of Alexandria with the intention that she should be converted into a floating oceanographic museum.

References:
Burstyn, 1975; Deacon and Rice, 1984; Girdler, 1984; Rice, 1986; White, 1984.

MALLARD

Steam yacht, built at Leith in 1878, 57 registered tons, 89' long, 14' beam, 25 h.p.

The vessel was built for John Young Buchanan who had been the chemist during the *Challenger* Expedition, and was intended specifically for oceanographic work. Between 1878 and 1882 Buchanan made a number of cruises to the west coast of Scotland and in the first of these found large numbers of small manganese nodules in Loch Fyne.

References:
Buchanan, 1919; Deacon, 1971; McConnell, 1982; Milne, 1972.

Manihine *at Mombassa. Courtesy Dr. J.H. Wickstead.*

MANIHINE

Converted trawler, built by the Goole Shipbuilding and Repairing Company 1906, 118′ long overall, 21′ beam, 208 tons gross.

The vessel was built originally as the steam trawler *Coot* and was purchased by Major H.W. Hall in 1938 and converted into a yacht under the name *Dorade II.* At this time her engines were replaced by twin diesels, each of 220 b.h.p. During the second world war she was requisitioned by the Royal Navy for work at Milford Haven and in Iceland.

In 1947 the vessel was renamed *Manihine* and made available from time to time to the British Museum (Natural History) for biological investigations. Most of the resulting cruises were confined to the English Channel, and particularly the eastern half. However, the *Manihine* carried out biological and hydrological work in the Gulf of Aqaba during the winter of 1948-49, and in the Sudanese Red Sea in 1950-51, in both cases under the command of Capt. Thomas Hargreaves and with N.B. Marshall representing the Natural History Museum.

Manihine was purchased and refitted for the Singapore Regional Fisheries Research Station in 1954, arriving in Singapore in 1955, and in 1957 she was transferred to the East African Marine Fisheries Research Organization (EAMFRO) based in Zanzibar.

In the early 1970s the vessel was purchased by a private businessman and converted into a combined passenger and cargo vessel in which capacity she operated between Zanzibar and Dar-es-Salaam for some years. At the time of writing she was lying in Dar-es-Salaam harbour more or less a hulk.

References:

East African Marine Fisheries Research Organization, 1958; Marshall, 1950, 1952.

H.M.S. Medea *towing a Turkish corvette out of a dangerous situation in the Island of Syra, 26 August 1836. Courtesy National Maritime Museum. Neg. no. 8168.*

HMS MEDEA

Wooden paddle sloop, 2-10inch, 2-32 pdr, built Woolwich 1833, 835 (bm), 179'4.5" long, 31'11" beam, 350 n.h.p., sold 1867.

The *Medea* was used in 1834 for early, unsuccessful, tests off the Isles of Scilly of the use of wire instead of rope for soundings.

Reference:
McConnell, 1982.

HMS MEDINA

Wooden paddle packet, built Pembroke Dock 1840, 889 (bm), 176' long, 33' beam, 312 n.h.p. Originally built as a mail packet, the *Medina* worked between Holyhead and Dublin until 1848 and thereafter in the Mediterranean. From 1856 to 1863 she was used as a survey vessel in the Mediterranean under Capt. Thomas Spratt.

Spratt had served under Graves in the *Beacon* from 1836-46, including the period in 1841-42 when Edward Forbes had joined the ship as naturalist. Spratt's interest in marine science had begun during his association with Forbes and had developed during his subsequent command of the *Spitfire* from 1851-1855. The *Spitfire* had been occupied entirely with shallow-water surveying, but Spratt's attention was drawn to deep-sea sounding by the general interest in such soundings during this period and particularly by the work of the U.S. Navy publicised by Matthew Fontaine Maury (see also under *Cyclops*). Consequently, he had his blacksmith produce a new sounding instrument, Bonnici's claw, as an improvement on the weight releasing device invented by John Brooke and widely used at the time.

Shortly after taking command of the *Medina,* Spratt made four deep soundings between Malta and the Greek Archipelago and in May 1857 he made a further line of soundings from Malta to Crete, including a deepest sounding at 2,200 fathoms (4024m), and then to Psara in the Greek Islands.

H.M.S. Medina. *Artist Dutton. Courtesy National Maritime Museum. Neg. no. 3326.*

In obtaining these soundings Spratt had great difficulty in taking samples of the sediment at the same time, both when using a Brooke sounder or Bonnici's claw, the latter being less successful than he had expected. Consequently, he separated the two operations, favouring the use of light silk line or twine for obtaining soundings since he believed that erroneously deep-soundings were caused by using lines which were so heavy that the effect of the weight of the line exceeded that of the weight at the bottom. In this belief he was at variance with Maury who had argued that such erroneous soundings were caused by sub-surface currents carrying the sounding line sideways. Spratt believed that significant undercurrents did not exist and carried out a number of experiments in 1857 with weights suspended at various levels beneath surface floats to test his ideas. The results seemed to confirm his beliefs and ultimately led to a major controversy during the early 1870s with W.B. Carpenter who took the contrary and, as it turned out, the correct view.

In 1858-59 the *Medina* was involved in the laying of several short telegraph cables in the Greek Archipelago and then with the disastrous attempt to lay a cable from Crete to Alexandria along the direct route across the deep eastern basin which had been surveyed by Mansell in the *Tartarus* in 1857. Three attempts to lay the cable were made by the cable ship *Elba,* all ending in failure.

Spratt felt that wherever possible such cables should be laid in comparatively shallow water and this policy was adopted in 1861 when the Malta to Alexandria cable was laid. The cable was laid from Malta to Tripoli and then along a route surveyed by Spratt in the *Medina* off the North African coast.

References:
Deacon, 1971, 1978; Spratt, 1857, 1865.

MEDUSA

Steam yacht (a screw smack in Lloyd's Yacht Register), built 1884 by J. McAdam at Govan, registered tonnage 14.62 (net), 23.44 (gross), 52' long, 12' beam, 14 h.p. engines by Paul and Co., Dumbarton.

The *Medusa* was commissioned by John Murray as the principal research vessel of the Scottish Marine Station for Scientific Research at Granton on the Firth of Forth. The station, which was opened in April 1884 and was at its most active between then and 1888, had been founded by Murray with the aid of grants from the Scottish Meteorological Society and from private individuals. Laurence Pullar, a boyhood friend of Murray with whom he had dredged in the Firth of Forth and sailed to the Western Isles, gave £1,000 towards the cost of the *Medusa.*

The building of the vessel was negotiated by D. & W. Henderson and Co., Engineers and Iron Shipbuilders, of Partick, Glasgow, who also undertook her later fitting out and maintenance throughout her oceanographic career. Murray was a friend of the family and in 1889 married Isabel Henderson, daughter of Thomas Henderson, brother of David and William, and founder of the Anchor Line of steamships.

H.R. Mill described the *Medusa* as "a beautiful little steam yacht... provided with arrangements for sounding, taking the temperature of the water, dredging and trawling, very conveniently installed but keeping to the old hemp lines for sounding and temperature work... Still, the old methods did well enough in the shallow waters we were to explore." But the fact that the *Medusa* could not be used in the open sea restricted her usefulness on the east coast where fisheries problems were attracting attention, and also government grants.

In the summer of 1885, however, Murray had the *Ark,* a floating laboratory which had provided the station's first base, towed from Granton Quarry to Millport on the Firth of Clyde. Here the *Medusa* found her *metier* and from 1886 to 1892 she was based at Millport "almost continually employed in exploring the shallow waters and deep land-locked sea-lochs of the coasts of Scotland", particularly of the Clyde Sea area, with a small crew headed by her captain, Alexander Turbyne. Murray was often on board, as was the Millport naturalist, David Robertson. The bulk of the work was carried out by scientists attached to the Scottish Marine Station and to the Challenger Expedition Office, which Murray directed. However, many visitors also sailed in the *Medusa,* including Ernst Haeckel and Alexander Agassiz. The physical results were worked up by Mill and appeared in the *Transactions of the Royal Society of Edinburgh,* but the biological results remained unpublished at this stage.

The *Medusa's* scientific work appears to have come to an end when she was laid up at Granton in the autumn of 1892, a victim perhaps of Murray's struggle to finish the *Challenger* Report. She was apparently sold towards the end of 1895.

Other projects then claimed Murray's attention, but before he died in a car accident in 1914 he was planning to return to Millport to work up the biological results of the *Medusa* voyages in conjunction with a renewed study of the area. He had already made over *Ark* to the Marine Station founded there in 1896 (she was broken up in a gale in 1900). Murray's former secretary and assistant James Chumley took over the work and published a monograph on the *Medusa* results some years later.

References:
Boog Watson, 1969; Chumley, 1918; Cunningham, 1885; Deacon, pers. comm.; Mill, 1951; Milne, 1972; Pullar, 1910; Walker, 1984.

H.M.S. Nassau. *Courtesy Imperial War Museum. Neg. no. Q 40829.*

HMS NASSAU

Wooden screw gunvessel, completed as a survey ship, built Pembroke Dock 1866, 695 (bm), 900 tons displacement, 185' long, 28'6" beam, 150 h.p., complement 90.

The *Nassau* was employed from 1866 to 1869 under the command of Capt. R.C. Mayne in re-surveying the Strait of Magellan and the passage north into the Pacific. During this period she was accompanied by Dr. R.O. Cunningham, on the recommendation of the Director at Kew, to make botanical and marine biological collections. The Hydrographer, G.H. Richards, obtained from the Treasury a salary for Cunningham of £200 to be continued after the voyage to enable the results to be written up. The resulting extensive collections were deposited mainly in the British Museum.

From 1870 to 1873 the *Nassau* was under the command of William Chimmo on the China Station. On the passage out from England Chimmo obtained a series of deep sea soundings between Ceylon and Java and thence to Hong Kong. Chimmo obtained extensive sub-surface temperature measurements in the China and Sulu Sea. He found that the lower levels of the Sulu Sea, below the depth at which it is in connection with the open ocean, is at a constant temperature. These results supported W.B. Carpenter's suggestion of the existence of a general oceanic circulation, prompted by the results of the *Lightning* and *Porcupine* cruises and about to be further investigated during the *Challenger* voyage.

From 1873 to 1877 the *Nassau* was employed in surveying first off East Africa and then once more on the China Station.

The vessel was finally broken up in 1880.

References:
Carpenter, W.B. 1872; Day, 1967; Deacon, 1971; Ritchie, 1967.

HMS NEWPORT

Wooden screw survey vessel, built Pembroke Dock 1867, 425 (bm), 570 tons displacement, 145' long, 25'6" beam, 325 i.h.p., 80 n.h.p., originally a gun vessel, but completed in 1868 as a survey vessel, complement 60.

Command of the *Newport* was given to G.S. Nares who had returned to England in 1867 after surveying in Queensland waters in the *Salamander*. From 1868 to 1870 the *Newport* was used for surveying work in the Mediterranean. In 1868 a sounding survey was conducted for a submarine telegraph cable between Malta and Alexandria, and in the autumn of that year the *Newport* assisted in laying the cable. In 1869 and 1870 Nares carried out further surveying off the Sicilian and north African coasts, including a route for a proposed cable between Sicily and Tunisia.

In November 1869 the *Newport* was one of the first ships through the Suez Canal following the French Imperial Yacht *L'Aigle*. In autumn 1870 the ship passed through the canal again to work in the Red Sea. In 1871 Nares left the *Newport* to take command of the *Shearwater*. The *Newport* does not seem to have been used subsequently for survey work and she was sold in 1881 and renamed *Pandora*.

The vessel was subsequently purchased by F. Leybourne Popham, renamed *Blencathra* and registered as a yacht from 1892 to 1898. In 1893 the *Blencathra* was contracted to the Russian Government to carry 1600 tons of rails to Siberia for the Trans-Siberian Railway. In her account of this voyage Helen Peel mistakenly identifies the *Blencathra* with Allen Young's *Pandora* (q.v.), presumably confused by the similarity of the two vessels and the fact that the *Newport* carried the name *Pandora* at one stage.

In 1898 the *Blencathra* sailed to Novaya Zemlya with Andrew Coats (see also under *Scotia*). W.S. Bruce, later to lead the Scottish National Antarctic Expedition, participated in this cruise in place of Coat's first choice, H.R. Mill, who was unable to go.

References:
Brown, 1923; Deacon and Savours, 1976; Peel, 1894.

NIMROD

Wooden screw barque, built by Alexander Stephen and Sons, Dundee, 1866, 136' long, 27' beam, 834 tons gross, 50 h.p. engines.

The *Nimrod* was employed in the Newfoundland seal industry from 1867 until 1907 when she was purchased for the Antarctic Expedition under Ernest Shackleton, having been fitted with new 60 h.p. engines, built by Westray, Copeland and Co. in 1889. Shackleton had hoped to be able to obtain the Norwegian vessel *Bjorn,* a newly built ship specially designed for polar work, but he could not afford her and had to take the 40-year-old *Nimrod* instead.

Having been invalided home from Scott's National Antarctic Expedition in the *Discovery,* Shackleton was determined to return to the Antarctic with his own expedition. His attempts to obtain financial backing from British institutions, including the Royal Geographical Society, were unsuccessful and the expedition was backed entirely by private benefactors until Shackleton received support from the Governments of Australia and New Zealand during his passage south.

Nevertheless, the Royal Geographical Society gave some moral support and forwarded his request for help to the Admiralty as a result of which he received the loan of a variety of instruments, including deep sea thermometers and a sounding machine. For although Shackleton's main objective was to reach the South Pole, he was anxious also to make a significant scientific contribution. Consequently, he assembled a very powerful scientific team, including Sir Philip Brocklehurst as a geologist, Raymond Priestley as mineralogist and James Murray as the biologist. In addition, when the ship reached New Zealand Shackleton also enlisted T.W. Edgeworth David, a professor at the University of Sydney, as chief geologist, and Douglas Mawson, then a lecturer at the University of Adelaide, as physicist. However, all

Nimrod. *Courtesy National Maritime Museum. Neg. no. P 823.*

of these specialists were to be included in the shore party so that the oceanographic work carried out from the *Nimrod* was very limited.

The ship sailed from England for New Zealand on 7 August 1907 under the command of Rupert G. England.   She left Lyttelton on 1 January 1908, being towed for the first 1500 miles, beyond the Antarctic Circle, by the steamer *Koonya,* the cost of the tow being shared by the New Zealand Government and Sir James Mills of the Union Steamship Company.

Shackleton had intended to establish his antarctic base at Barrier (or Balloon) Inlet in the Ross Ice Barrier, originally seen from *Discovery.*   However, when he reached the locality of the inlet he found that the Barrier had changed and that the inlet had been replaced by a much larger bay which he named the Bay of Whales and which Amundsen later used for his Framheim base.   Shackleton's second choice for a base, King Edward VII Land, was also unsuitable because of the ice conditions and he was finally forced to winter at Cape Royds, on Ross Island, where Scott's base had been established.

Having landed the men and stores, the *Nimrod* left on 22 February 1908 and sailed direct to New Zealand.   Here she stayed throughout the southern winter until 1 December 1908 when she sailed for her second antarctic voyage to collect the shore party.   England had resigned due to ill health when the *Nimrod* had reached New Zealand after the first voyage and the ship was now under the command of F.P. Evans who had been captain of the *Koonya* during the outward tow the year before.

After a series of vicissitudes the vessel picked up all of the shore parties and left Cape Royds on 4 March.   An attempt to explore the coastline of Victoria Land to the west of Cape North was unsuccessful and the *Nimrod* returned to New Zealand, arriving at Lyttelton on 25 March 1909.

The Expedition had been a great success. The southern party, led by Shackleton, had reached a point only 97 miles from the South Pole, a second party had reached the magnetic pole, while a third group had climbed Mount Erebus, its first ascent. Furthermore, the scientific team had made extensive geological, meteorological, magnetic and biological observations.

However, although Shackleton's narrative includes a few references to soundings having been taken, there are no extensive references to oceanographic observations from the *Nimrod*. Moreover, the Report on the scientific results of the Expedition, published in four volumes (two on biology and two on geology) between 1910 and 1916, contains no strictly oceanographic results. However, Murray organised extensive marine collecting, the samples ultimately being deposited in the British Museum (Natural History). These collections were made mainly through the sea ice in a small bay close to the winter quarters between Cape Royds and Cape Barne. Baited traps were lowered through holes in the ice and caught fish, amphipods, molluscs and worms, while other benthic animals were collected by dredging between two holes, 50 to 100 yards apart, using a similar technique to that employed by Hodgson during the National Antarctic Expedition in the *Discovery* from 1901 to 1904. As the *Nimrod* sailed through the Ross Sea, plankton townets were used on several occasions and while she was moored to the ice in the middle of McMurdo Sound a number of vertical hauls were made from depths down to about 400m. This technique could not be used through the ice holes because the depth was generally insufficient.

After the Antarctic Expedition the *Nimrod* was sold to a South African company in 1910 and was used for the Webster Expedition to the Yenessi River in Siberia in 1911. During the First World War the vessel served as a coastal collier registered in Dundee and was finally wrecked at Caister, Yarmouth, in January 1919 with the loss of ten crew members.

References:

British Antarctic Expedition, 1907-1909; Henderson, pers. comm., Dundee Museum; Huntford, 1985; Shackleton, 1909.

NORNA

Yacht owned by Marshall Hall, a wealthy barrister, used for deep-sea dredging off the coasts of Spain and Portugal in May and June 1870 under the supervision of W. Saville Kent, of the Department of Geology at the British Museum (Natural History). Kent received a grant of £50 from the Royal Society to help defray the costs of the dredging equipment.

The visit to the Iberian coast was prompted by the results of earlier work in the same area. In 1864 Prof. Barboza du Bocage, Director of the Natural History Museum in Lisbon, had announced the discovery of siliceous spicules, similar to those of the glass sponge *Hyalonema* known previously only from Japanese waters, in samples obtained from the Setubal shark-fishers. These fishermen worked in very deep water, supposedly down to 500 fathoms (915m), and E. Perceval Wright and Bocage visited the fishing grounds in 1868 and successfully dredged complete specimens of the sponge. The *Norna* expedition was intended to continue and extend this work.

After stopping at Guernsey for some shore collecting, the *Norna* proceeded to Vigo where extensive shallow water dredging was undertaken in Vigo Bay, followed by a series of hauls down to about 800 fathoms (c. 1460m) off Setubal in southern Portugal.

Kent published an account of the glass sponges collected during the expedition later the same year, and a general account of the collections in 1871, encouraging "British pluck and private enterprise" to undertake similar work in the future. However, although the *Norna* collections seem largely to have found their way to the British Museum (Natural History) over the next decade, either by gift or by purchase, few of the groups seem to have been reported on.

References:
Kent, 1870, 1871.

OCEANA

Steel twin-screw vessel built by Gourlay Bros. and Co., Dundee, 1889, 311 tons gross, 140' long, 22'6" beam, 112 n.h.p.

In November 1898 the *Oceana* was used for a cruise to the south-west of Ireland, financed by grants from the Royal Geographical Society, the Drapers' Company and the Fishmongers' Company. The cruise was under the direction of George Murray from the British Museum, accompanied by L. Fletcher, J.W. Gregory and V.H. Blackman, also from the British Museum, and by J.E.S. Moore from the Royal College of Science.

The aim of the cruise was to investigate the existence of the so-called intermediate fauna in the deep water column of the open ocean. On the basis of the *Challenger* Expedition results using open townets, Wyville Thomson had first proposed that these regions were devoid of life and this idea had been taken up by Alexander Agassiz with support from his own experiments using closing nets from the U.S. vessels *Blake* and *Albatross*.

John Murray, on the other hand, had interpreted the *Challenger* results quite differently, concluding that mid-water life existed at all depths in the ocean. This view was adopted in Europe by Carl Chun using supporting evidence obtained during the Italian circumnavigation in the *Vettor Pisani* in 1882-1884 and his own experiments with closing nets in the Mediterranean in 1886 and later during the *Valdivia* Expedition in 1898-1899.

Whether or not the intermediate fauna existed was an important element in discussions about how the deep-sea communities living on and close to the sea-floor were nourished. If the intermediate layers were truly barren, then the deep-living communities must be supported entirely by the remains of organisms sinking from the productive surface layers. If, on the other hand, the intermediate layers were populated, then the transfer of material between the surface and the bottom could be augmented by the vertical migrations of the members of the intermediate fauna.

Ultimately Agassiz was shown to be wrong in that the whole water column is occupied in most regions of the oceans. His failure to find an intermediate fauna resulted partly from deficiencies in the nets he used and partly from the peculiarities of the regions in which he worked.

On the *Oceana* cruise serial townettings with open townets were carried out to a maximum depth of 1835 fathoms (3358m), while hauls were also attempted with opening and closing nets, one a Tanner net as used by Agassiz, the other specially made for the cruise by M.H. Gray.

In its main aim the cruise was not very successful. The results obtained with the Tanner net were disappointing and suggested that it was not working efficiently, while the Gray net seemed promising but was put out of action early by bad weather. Inclement weather also prevented the use of fish traps.

The vessel had been equipped with Sigsbee sounding machines and Miller-Casella thermometers which were used routinely. Murray describes how the soundings all had to be hove in by hand, the members of the expedition taking turns in pairs at this task. The exhausted condition of Murray himself and Captain Rickman during the first shallow sounding caused dismay among the other participants at the prospect of doing the same job on the later soundings–until it was discovered that the captain and the principal scientist had been working with the brake on!

References:

Mills, 1980; Murray, G. 1899.

H.M.S. Ormonde *photographed in 1931. Courtesy National Maritime Museum. Neg. no. N 4086.*

HMS ORMONDE

"24" class minesweeping sloop, built Blyth 1918, 1650 tons displacement, 267'6" long, 35' beam, 2500 i.h.p.

The *Ormonde* was converted to a survey vessel in 1924 and in April and May 1927 was used for hydrographical work in the Straits of Bab-el-Mandeb and the Gulf of Aden under the command of C.W. Rice.   The results agreed with the earlier winter and spring observations from the *Pola* (1897-1898), *Vitiaz* (1899), *Stork* (1898) and *Ammiraglio Magnaghi* (1924), indicating a surface flow into the Red Sea and a deep, warm, high salinity current into the Gulf.   A more complex three tier system, with surface and deep currents flowing into the Gulf and an intermediate current into the Red Sea, was revealed by the observations during the John Murray / Mabahiss expedition in September 1933.

The *Ormonde* was sold in 1937.

Reference:

Matthews, 1927, 1928.

PAGODA

Barque built at Hylton, Co. Durham, 1844, 362 tons, hired by the Admiralty to carry out a cruise in high southern latitudes in 1845. At the suggestion of Edward Sabine, the objective of the voyage was to make magnetic observations to fill in gaps left by James Clark Ross in the *Erebus* and *Terror* in 1839-43, between the Greenwich meridian and 120°E.

Under the command of Lieut. T.E.L. Moore, the *Pagoda* left England in January 1845 and, after calling at South Africa, made first for Bouvetøya (Bouvet Island), which could not be found, and then for the western end of Enderby Land. Adverse winds, currents and ice conditions prevented Moore from landing, but he sailed eastward in high latitudes to 100°E, off what is now known as Queen Mary Land, which he reached on 11 March, before turning northwards, away from the ice. After calling at Albany in Western Australia, Moore sailed back to Simon's Bay via Mauritius, arriving on 20 June.

Here the voyage officially ended, Moore leaving the vessel in the command of her owner, Henry Byron, who had sailed with him as master. The *Pagoda* left Simon's Bay for Mauritius and was lost on 26 January 1846.

Apart from the magnetic, meteorological and hygrometric observations, Moore made a few moderately deep soundings, and threw bottles overboard in an attempt to determine surface currents. However, no significant oceanographic observations were made.

References:

Jones, 1970; Moore, 1846.

H.M.S. Pandora *(1833). Artist N.M. Condy. Courtesy National Maritime Museum. Neg. no. 8315.*

HMS PANDORA

Brig, 3-32 pdr, built Woolwich 1833 and completed as a packet, 319 (bm), 90′ long, 29′ beam, design complement 50-60, converted to a survey ship 1845.

Under the command of Lt. Cdr. James Wood the *Pandora* was used as tender to H.M.S.

Herald during her circumnavigation in 1845-1848. Natural history collections made from the vessel were deposited in the British Museum. The *Pandora* and *Herald* parted company in 1848 when the latter was ordered to participate in the search for Sir John Franklin. The *Pandora* became a coastguard watch vessel in 1857 and was sold in 1862.

Reference:
Seeman, 1853.

HMS PANDORA

Wooden screw "Philomel" class gunvessel, 1-68 pdr, 2-24 pdr, 2-20 pdr, built Pembroke Dock 1861, 428 (bm), 570 tons gross, 145′ long, 25′6″ beam, 307 i.h.p., 80 n.h.p., complement 60.

The *Pandora* was commissioned in 1863 and served off the coast of Africa until 1867. In 1875 she was purchased by Sir Allen Young and refitted in Southampton for Arctic exploration. During the summers of 1875 and 1876 Young used her for two expeditions principally in search of the north-west passage, but also to look for relics of the Franklin Expedition in the *Erebus* and *Terror*. Young had no intention of wintering in the Arctic, though he took sufficient stores in case this should be necessary. On the first cruise the *Pandora* passed through Lancaster Sound and into Peel Sound, but in the following year Young was asked to try to make contact with the Arctic Expedition under Nares in the *Alert* and *Discovery* (q.v.). Accordingly, in 1876 the *Pandora* spent several weeks unsuccessfully waiting for Nares who actually returned home, having cut his expedition short, while Young was still waiting.

H.M.S. Pandora *(1861). Artist T.C.D. Thompson. Courtesy National Maritime Museum. Neg. no. A 1845.*

The expenses of the voyages were met mainly by Young himself, but with contributions from Franklin's widow, from James Gordon Bennett (who sent J.A. MacGahan as his correspondent), and from Lieut. F. Innes Lillingston who sailed as second-in-command during the 1875 voyage.

On both voyages Young was accompanied by George Pirie, a Royal Naval surveying officer who had served previously on the *Porcupine* and was given permission to join the *Pandora* by the Admiralty.   Pirie carried out magnetic observations, while meteorological and natural history investigations, including townet sampling, were conducted by Dr. Arthur C. Horner who sailed as surgeon and naturalist.   Some hydrographic work was also carried out, including soundings and sub-surface temperature measurements.

The *Pandora* was subsequently renamed *Jeanette* and used for the U.S. Expedition towards the North Pole via Bering Strait under Lieut. De Long in 1879-1881.   The vessel became ice-bound south-east of Wrangel Island (Ostrov Vrangelya) in September 1879 and drifted west-north-westerly for two years until she foundered and broke up north of New Siberia in June 1881.   Three years later wreckage from the ship was found near Julianehaab in south-west Greenland and this prompted Fridtjof Nansen to organise his famous expedition in the *Fram* in 1893-1896.

Peel's (1894) statement that the yacht *Blencathra* was Young's *Pandora* is clearly an error. The *Blencathra* was actually H.M.S. *Newport* (q.v.) which was very similar to the *Pandora* and was herself confusingly renamed *Pandora* when she was first sold by the Admiralty in 1881.

References:
Day, 1967; MacGahan, 1976; Nansen, 1898; Peel, 1894; Preston and Major, 1967; Young, 1877.

H.M.S. Penguin. *Courtesy National Maritime Museum. Neg. no. N 5456.*

HMS PENGUIN

Composite screw sloop, 2-7inch, 4-64 pdr, built Napier 1876, 1130 tons displacement, 170′ long, 36′ beam, 720 i.h.p., complement 140-150.

The *Penguin* became a survey vessel in 1890 and worked mainly in Australian waters and in the southwestern Pacific under the command of Commander W. Usborne Moore from 1890 to

1893 and under Commander A.F. Balfour from 1893 to 1895. In addition, at the instigation of the Hydrographer, W.J.L. Wharton, Moore had also investigated the currents in the Strait of Bab-el-Mandeb.

In 1892 Surgeon P.W. Bassett-Smith obtained zoological samples on the Macclesfield Bank from the *Penguin,* continuing his earlier work from H.M.S. *Rambler* in 1888.

In 1895 Balfour made three soundings from the *Penguin* in over 5000 fathoms (9145m) in the Kermadec Trench, the deepest obtained to that date.

In 1896 a party under W.J. Sollas, Professor of Palaeontology at Oxford, embarked on the *Penguin,* under Capt. A.M. Field, for an unsuccessful attempt to obtain borings at Funafuti Atoll. Sollas was accompanied by J. Stanley Gardiner who made a number of expeditions to the Indian Ocean and Pacific from 1897 and was the scientific leader of the Percy Sladen Trust Expedition in the *Sealark* in 1905.

The *Penguin* became a depot ship at Sydney in 1908 and was transferred to the Royal Australian Navy in 1913. She was sold in 1924, became a crane hulk and was burnt in 1960.

References:
Bassett-Smith, 1895; Day, 1967; Deacon, 1971; Somerville, 1928; Wharton, 1896, 1898.

HMS PHEASANT

"Merlin" class sloop, 16-6 pdr, 6-12 pdr carronades, built by Edwards, Shoreham 1798, 365 (bm), 106′ long, 28′ beam, design complement 21.

Between February 1822 and February 1823 Capt. Edward Sabine joined the *Pheasant,* under the command of Cdr. D.C. Clavering, for a cruise off the coast of West Africa and in the Caribbean. Sabine's main objective was to carry out pendulum observations continuing those he had made in the Arctic during Ross's voyage in the *Isabella* and *Alexander* in 1818 and with Parry in the *Hecla* and *Griper* in 1819-1820. Sabine was originally to have carried out his observations from *Iphigenia,* but during the passage out to West Africa he decided to transfer to the *Pheasant,* possibly as a result of meeting Clavering who was also travelling on the H.M.S. *Iphigenia* to take up his new command (see Jones, 1976).

In addition to his pendulum observations, Sabine made two measurements of deep sub-surface temperatures, once at 1250 fathoms (2286m) and once at 650 fathoms (1189m), the second designed to investigate the effect of water pressure on unprotected thermometers. Sabine wrongly concluded that there was no such pressure effect and his results confirmed him in his erroneous view that sea-water has a maximum density at about 40°F, and thus behaves rather like freshwater. Sabine had clung to this false idea despite his presence on the *Isabella* when much lower temperatures had been recorded in Baffin's Bay in 1818, and Marcet's 1819 paper, based partly on the *Isabella* results, which had clearly demonstrated that sea water continues to increase in density until it freezes.

The *Pheasant* was hulked at Woolwich in 1824 as a temporary receiving ship, and was sold in 1827.

References:
Deacon, 1971; Sabine, 1823.

HMS PIKE

Schooner, 2-6 pdr, 12-12 pdr carronades, built New Orleans 1813 as the American vessel *Dart,* captured in 1813, 251 (bm), 93′ long, 24′8″ beam, complement 60.

The *Pike* carried out extensive sounding surveys in relatively shallow water around the British Isles in 1831 under the command of Capt. A.T.E. Vidal. These soundings revealed extensive areas of shell sands and gravels on the Rockall Bank, a very early record of such carbonate sediments.

The *Pike* was wrecked in 1836 and the wreck was sold.

References:
Lyell (1833); Wilson (1979).

POLAR STAR

Dundee whaler, under the command of James Davidson, which accompanied the *Balaena* (q.v.) to the Antarctic in 1892-1893.

HMS PORCUPINE

Wooden two-masted brigantine-rigged paddle gun-vessel, built Deptford Dockyard 1844, 382 (bm), 490 tons displacement, 141′ long, 24′ beam. Side lever engine by Maudslay, Son and Field, 132 n.h.p., 285 i.h.p. The engine had been installed originally in the *Columbia* in 1829 and was at that time rated at 120 n.h.p. It was removed in 1832, overhauled and installed in the *Firebrand,* the predecessor of the ship of that name dealt with in this volume. In 1843 the engine was once more removed and repaired. The effective diameter of the cylinders was increased, thus raising the nominal horse power, and it was installed in the *Porcupine* in 1844.

The vessel was commissioned initially for survey work in the Thames Estuary and was sent to the Mediterranean in 1847, returning to Portsmouth in 1851. She served in the Baltic in 1854 under the command of H.C. Otter. In 1856 she became the principal naval survey vessel in

H.M.S. Porcupine. *Reproduced by permission of the Hydrographer to the Navy. In view of the importance of the* Porcupine *in the history of oceanography it is particularly regrettable that this poor quality photograph seems to be the only illustration of the vessel in existence.*

home waters, taking over this role from the *Shearwater*. In 1858, again under Otter, the *Porcupine*, together with the *Gorgon* under Dayman, assisted the *Niagara* and the *Agamemnon* to lay the transatlantic telegraph cable which remained in operation for only a few weeks.

In 1862 the vessel worked off the south west of Ireland under Capt. Richard Hoskyn in an attempt to find a less precipitous route off the continental shelf for the projected replacement transatlantic cable. Hoskyn discovered a suitable route to the west of Slyne Head via the Porcupine Bank on which he carried out some dredging. He also tested Johnson's metallic thermometers, which he thought worked well, and both Johnson's and Hearder's pressure gauges, which did not. A preliminary report on the sediment and dredging samples was published by William King as an appendix to Hoskyn's general report on the voyage. Hoskyn informed the Hydrographer that the bad weather experienced had prevented him making more extensive use of the dredge.

From 1863 the *Porcupine* reverted to more conventional surveying around the British coasts under Staff Cdr. and later Capt. Edward Killiwick Calver until her series of oceanographic cruises in 1869 and 1870.

Following the limited success but encouraging results obtained by C. Wyville Thomson and W.B. Carpenter in the *Lightning* in 1868, the Royal Society established a Committee on Marine Researches, with the Hydrographer, Capt. G.H. Richards, as one of the members. The Society approached the Admiralty with a proposal for a further cruise, and the *Porcupine* was

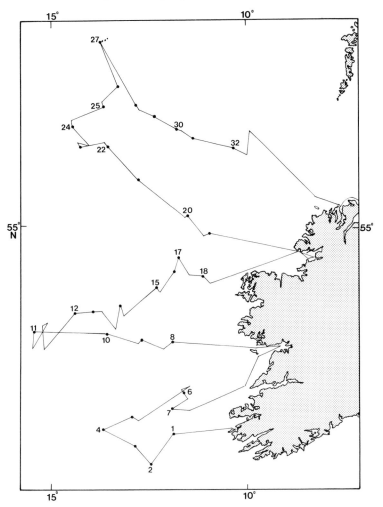

Track of H.M.S. Porcupine *to the west of Ireland during May to July, 1869, with the station positions marked. Redrawn from Thomson, 1873, plate II.*

made available from mid May to mid September 1869. Since neither Wyville Thomson nor Carpenter could spare this length of time from their official duties, it was decided to divide the available time into three cruises, the first to be taken by John Gwyn Jeffreys, with Carpenter's eldest son, William Lant Carpenter, to be responsible for the physical and chemical work.

There were two principal objectives of the *Porcupine* cruise; first to dredge in really deep water, well beyond the 650 fathoms (1189m) achieved from the *Lightning*, and second to investigate in more detail the cold and warm areas encountered by the *Lightning* in the Faröe-Shetland Channel. For improved deep temperature measurements, the instrument maker Casella had made maximum / minimum thermometers with thickened bulbs and others in which the conventional bulb was enclosed within a second one partially filled with alcohol, at the suggestion of William Allen Miller, professor of chemistry at King's College, London. This second type, which became known as the Miller-Casella thermometer, was less affected by pressure and was used for almost all of the temperature measurements made during the *Challenger* Expedition.

After coaling at Galway, the first cruise consisted of three loops off the west coast of Ireland, the first from Dingle Bay out to the southern part of the Porcupine Bank and back into Galway Bay, then out over the shallowest part of the bank into the Rockall Trough and back into Donegal Bay, and finally across to Rockall Bank and back to Lough Swilly and thence to Belfast. Some 32 deep stations were worked, including many dredge hauls, the deepest at 1476 fathoms (2700m), and many deep temperature measurements in which the Miller-Casella thermometers recorded lower temperatures than the unprotected instruments with which they were compared.

The second cruise, from 17 July to 4 August, was under the scientific direction of Wyville Thomson, with a chemical assistant from the University of Belfast and with Carpenter's younger son Philip Herbert Carpenter learning the chemical techniques in preparation for the third cruise on which he was to accompany his father. The original intention was for this second cruise to attempt deep dredging to the west of the Outer Hebrides, but the dredging work on the first cruise had been so successful that Thomson was anxious to extend their efforts to the deepest water they could reach. Accordingly, after consulting Calver and obtaining the approval of Richards, the *Porcupine* made for a point 250 miles to the west of Ushant, off what is now known as the Pendragon Escarpment to the south of the Goban Spur. Here, on 22

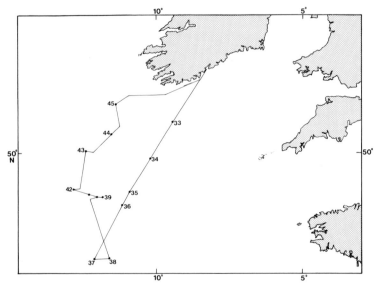

Track of H.M.S. Porcupine *to the south-west of Ireland during July and August 1869, with the station positions marked. Redrawn from Thomson, 1873, plate III.*

July, at a depth of 2453 fathoms (4289m), they completed by far the deepest dredge haul ever attempted, obtaining a mass of mud and a wide range of animals and thus finally dispelling the azoic theory.

A second very deep dredge haul was obtained at a depth of 2090 fathoms (3823m) and the ship then worked a series of shallower stations through the Porcupine Seabight and returned to Queenstown and then Belfast. Here the ship stayed for a week to clean her boilers and she then sailed to Stornoway to begin her final cruise of the year with Carpenter, Thomson and Carpenter's son.

Between 15 August, when the ship left Stornoway, and the 15 September when she finally returned to Belfast, the *Porcupine* worked a total of 45 stations in three legs, the first between Stornoway and Thorshavn in the Faröes, the second back across the Faröe-Shetland Channel to Lerwick, and the third zig-zagging along the south-eastern border of the Channel back to Stornoway. Some of these stations were in relatively shallow water, particularly those to the east of the Shetlands, but the majority were within the Channel in depths down to rather more than 700 fathoms (1280m). As during the *Lightning* cruise, they found two distinct areas, separated by only a few miles, in which the water column seemed to be relatively warm or relatively cold irrespective of depth. Captain Calver suggested the addition of stranded hemp "tangles" to the dredge to improve its efficiency on the hard, stony sea-bed in the cold area. The tangles demonstrated that while the animal populations in the two kinds of environment were quite different, the fauna of the cold area was not as sparse as they had thought previously.

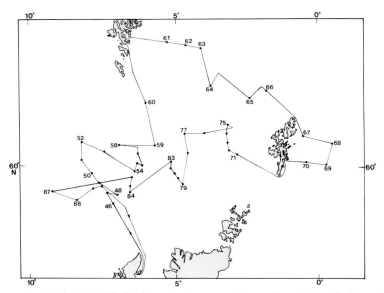

Track of H.M.S. Porcupine *in the Faröe-Shetland area in August and September, 1869, with the station positions marked. Redrawn from Thomson, 1873, plate IV.*

Carpenter interpreted the temperature results in terms of his ideas of a general oceanic circulation which had originated from the *Lightning* cruise. He thought that, apart from the very surface layers, the relatively warm water in the upper part of the water column had originated in equatorial regions. This water extended deeper in the "warm" than in the "cold" area where cold water of Arctic origin flowed in a southerly direction beneath it, penetrating into the Atlantic proper along a few channels in the generally shallow areas between Iceland, Greenland and mainland Europe. Carpenter thought that the cold deep water in the Atlantic had originated in the Antarctic.

Although this interpretation contained serious errors, Carpenter's belief in a deep circulation driven by density differences was eventually proved to be substantially correct. However, neither Thomson nor Gwyn Jeffreys would accept Carpenter's ideas and dissociated themselves from this part of the report on the 1869 cruises.

A new Royal Society Committee with both Carpenter and Gwyn Jeffreys as members was established to plan a further voyage, this time to the Mediterranean where Jeffreys was interested in the fauna while Carpenter wished to look for evidence of an undercurrent through the Strait of Gibraltar. The *Porcupine,* once again under Calver, was made available from July to October 1870. As in the previous year, the intention was to divide the voyage into three sections, but Thomson was taken ill and was therefore unable to take part so that Gwyn Jeffreys took the first leg, from Falmouth to Gibraltar, while Carpenter took the whole of the second part for all of the work in the Mediterranean.

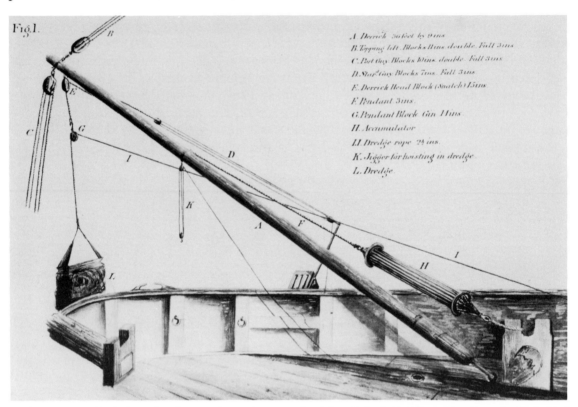

Deck arrangement for dredging aboard H.M.S. Porcupine. *Reproduced from Calver's 1869* Porcupine Journal *with the kind permission of the Hydrographer to the Navy.*

The *Porcupine* left Falmouth on July 4, Jeffreys being accompanied by the young Swedish naturalist Joshua Lindahl as zoological assistant and W.L. Carpenter as chemist. By the time they reached Gibraltar on August 6 they had worked 39 dredging stations in depths to a little over 1000 fathoms (1820m), mainly off the coast of the Iberian Peninsula and to the west of the Strait of Gibraltar, but a few in the northern Bay of Biscay.

Jeffreys was replaced by the elder Carpenter, as planned, at Gibraltar, but both Lindahl and Carpenter's son remained aboard. The ship left Gibraltar on August 15 and Carpenter immediately worked a station in the narrowest part of the Strait, at a depth of 517 fathoms (946m) to investigate the existence of an outflowing undercurrent. The temperature measurements revealed an almost uniform temperature from about 50 fathoms to the bottom, but the water samples showed a salinity maximum at about 250 fathoms (457m) where the water was much more dense than normally encountered Atlantic water. Carpenter was convinced that the outflowing current was in this warm, highly saline intermediate layer.   Experiments with a simple current drogue, made of sail cloth stretched across a pair of iron bars in the form of a cross, seemed to confirm this view; with the drogue at a depth of 100 fathoms and attached to a small boat, the boat moved with the inflowing surface current, but at about half its speed, interpreted as indicating that the drogue was in still water.   With the drogue at 250 fathoms, on the other hand, the boat scarcely moved at all, suggesting that the drogue was in water moving at more or less the same speed as the surface current, but in the opposite direction.

As they came back through the Strait at the end of the cruise the same station was re-examined.   The surface current was now rather weaker than before and, with the current drogue at 250 fathoms, the boat actually moved against the surface current.   Here appeared to be incontrovertible proof of the existence of a sub-surface outflow, but the results were not thought to be totally satisfactory at the time and the observations were repeated the following year from the *Shearwater.*

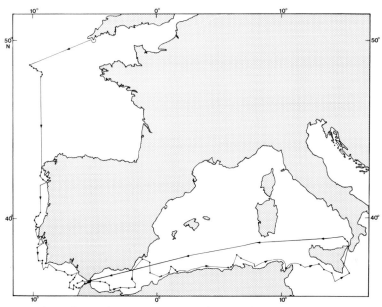

Track of H.M.S. Porcupine *during her Mediterranean cruise in July to October, 1870. Redrawn from Thomson, 1873, plate V.*

Between these two sets of observations in the Strait the *Porcupine* sailed along the north African coast to Tunis and Malta, along the east coast of Sicily and through the Strait of Messina and then back via the Strait of Gibraltar to England, arriving at Cowes on 8 October.   During the eastward track in the Mediterranean, soundings, serial temperatures and water samples were obtained at some 22 stations, and dredge hauls were taken down to about 1500 fathoms (2744m).   The dredge samples revealed that although life existed at great depths in the Mediterranean, it was very sparse compared with the Atlantic and some regions were almost azoic beyond a few hundred fathoms, as Forbes had suggested.   These biological results were therefore rather disappointing, but the physical results were much more interesting.   All of the temperature sections showed that there was little decrease below 50 to 100 fathoms and that the bottom water was relatively warm, the minimum temperature recorded being 54.5°F.   Moreover, the temperature and salinity characteristics of the outflowing intermediate layer found in the Strait were similar to the bottom waters in the shallower areas examined within the Mediterranean, whereas the lower salinity of the bottom water in the Strait was typical of the bottom water in the deeper areas of the Sea.   Carpenter interpreted these results in terms of his general oceanic circulation theory, and became embroiled in a major controversy with opponents of his ideas, including Thomson and Thomas Spratt, but particularly James Croll (see Deacon, 1971, p. 318 et seq.).

Despite this controversy, however, the cruises of the *Porcupine* had been a great success and led directly to the *Challenger* Expedition from 1872 to 1876. After her oceanographic cruises the vessel reverted to more conventional surveys in home waters until 1881 when she was succeeded by the *Triton* and was sold in 1883.

Most of the biological collections made from the *Porcupine,* and from the *Lightning* before her, were deposited in the natural history collections of the British Museum. Unfortunately, at some time in the past the samples from groups of stations were mixed, so that it is now impossible to determine the precise localities from which many individual specimens were obtained.

References:
Carpenter, Jeffreys and Thomson, 1869-1870; Carpenter and Jeffreys, 1870-71; Deacon, 1971; Thomson, 1873.

QUEST

Wooden vessel used for the Shackleton-Rowett Expedition to the South Atlantic and Weddell Sea, 1921-1922, backed by Shackleton's old school friend John Quiller Rowett.

The ship was built as the *Foca I* in Norway in 1890-1891 for Arctic sealing. She was 111' long, 23' beam, 125 tons, ketch rigged and with 120 h.p. auxillary steam engines.

Originally Shackleton intended to explore the Arctic, but delays in organizing the expedition caused him to miss the Arctic season and he decided to go south instead. The ship sailed from London via Lisbon, Madeira, the Cape Verdes and St. Paul's Rocks to Rio, where she refitted for a month before proceeding to South Georgia. Here Shackleton died of a heart attack on 5 January 1922. Frank Wild, who had been with Shackleton on the British Antarctic Expedition of 1907-1909, took over command and continued into the Weddell Sea and then worked along the pack ice towards Graham Land and thence to the South Shetlands, and home via South Georgia, Gough Island, Tristan da Cunha, Cape Town, St. Helena, Ascension Island and the Azores.

Apart from surveying, the expedition carried out hydrographic, magnetic and geological work and limited natural history, most of the results being published as appendices to Wild's account of the voyage.

During the voyage south, the third recorded landing on St Paul's Rocks was made, the two previous landings being during the voyages of the *Beagle* and the *Challenger.* The fourth landing was made during the cruise of H.M.S. *Owen,* under Commander G.P.D. Hall, in 1960-61.

After the Shackleton-Rowett Expedition the *Quest* reverted to her sealing role, but in 1930-31 she was used for the British Air Route Expedition under H.G. (Gino) Watkins. This expedition explored the east coast of Greenland, with two de Haviland Moth seaplanes, to investigate Watkins' ideas for an Arctic air route.

References:
Fisher and Fisher, 1957; Grierson, 1964; Smith, 1930; Tutein, 1938; Wild, 1923.

HMS RATTLESNAKE

"Atholl" class 6th rate, 2-9 pdr, 20-32 pdr carronades, 6-18 pdr carronades, built Chatham Dockyard 1822, 500 (bm), 113'8" long, 31'6" beam, design complement 175. The vessel became a troopship in 1839 and a survey vessel in 1846.

H.M.S. Rattlesnake. *Artist O.W. Brierly. Courtesy National Maritime Museum. Neg. no. X 1412.*

The *Rattlesnake* was sent to the south-western Pacific under Capt. Owen Stanley from December 1846 to 1850 to continue the surveying work of the *Fly* and particularly to survey a safe route through the Torres Strait and the Great Barrier Reef. The *Rattlesnake* was assigned the *Bramble* and *Castlereagh* as tenders.

Stanley's second in command was Lieut. Joseph Dayman who carried out extensive surface and sub-surface temperature measurements using Six thermometers and obtained soundings using a Massey sounding instrument (see McConnell, 1982).

Stanley died while the ship was at Sydney in March 1850 and the command for the return to England was given to Lieut. C.B. Yule, previously in command of the *Bramble*.

Extensive marine collections, including many with townets, were made during the commission by John MacGillivray as naturalist and Thomas Henry Huxley as Assistant Surgeon and naturalist. Unusually for the time, MacGillivray's appointment was specifically as naturalist and Huxley's was as assistant to the official ship's surgeon, a Dr. Thomson. Huxley's appointment had been recommended by Sir John Richardson under whom he had studied at the Royal Naval Hospital Haslar.

The vessel was not well provided with scientific equipment and MacGillivray and Huxley had to use considerable initiative. The townet was home made from ship's bunting attached to a 14″ wooden hoop, while for sieving dredge samples they used "a wire-gauze meat-cover and a curious machine for cleaning rice..." (Macgillivray, 1852).

The *Rattlesnake* was one of a series of surveying vessels which seem to have been less than ideal for the purposes for which they were used. Clearly Huxley was unimpressed:

"...Exploring vessels will be invariably found to be the slowest, clumsiest, and in every respect the most inconvenient ships which wear the pennant. In accordance with the rule, such was the *Rattlesnake;* and to carry out the spirit of the authorities more completely, she was turned out of Plymouth dockyard in such a disgraceful state of unfitness, that her lower deck was continually under water during the voyage."

The *Rattlesnake* was broken up at Chatham in 1860.

References:

Foster and Lankester, 1900; Huxley, L. 1900; Huxley, T.H. 1936; Johnson, 1976; Macgillivray, 1852.

RESEARCH

Cutter of 40 tons purchased in Malta 1846 by Capt. Thomas Graves to replace the *Isabella* as tender to the *Beacon.*

From 1846 to 1848 the *Research* was commanded by Thomas Spratt who continued the deep dredging work he had begun from the *Isabella* and the smaller tender *Fancy* during Edward Forbes' period with the *Beacon* in 1841 and 1842. Spratt's dredgings included one at 390 fathoms (713m), considerably deeper than the 300 fathom limit of life suggested by Forbes in formulating his azoic theory.

Reference:

Deacon, 1978.

H.M.S. Research *photographed in 1911. Courtesy National Maritime Museum. Neg. no. N 4075.*

HMS RESEARCH

Paddle survey vessel, built Chatham Dockyard 1888, 520 tons displacement, 155' long, 24' beam, 450 i.h.p. Apparently the vessel was named *Investigator* originally, but was renamed during building.

The *Research* was used for survey work, mainly in British waters, until she was paid off along with the *Triton* in 1914, the last two paddle vessels to be used by the Hydrographic Department (Day, 1967). She was sold in 1920.

During her first season, under the command of Pelham Aldrich, the *Research* was joined for 10 days by G. C. Bourne at the suggestion of the Hydrographer, W.J.L. Wharton, to obtain trawl samples off south-west Ireland while the vessel was principally engaged in a sounding survey. The *Research* was equipped with a steam winch, deep-sea trawls and dredges and 1000 fathoms (1800m) of wire rope. Bourne obtained a series of eight trawl samples from the Great Sole Bank and the eastern side of the Porcupine Seabight in depths ranging from about 70 to 400 fathoms (c. 128 to 730m) and also carried out a number of tow-net hauls.

In April-May 1896, under Capt. W. Usborne Moore, the vessel was used for current measurements in the Straits of Dover using a Pillsbury Current Meter recently acquired by the Royal Navy. Later the same year G. Herbert Fowler joined the *Research* for trials in the Faröe-Shetland Channel of a closing plankton net which he had designed to test Alexander Agassiz's belief that no pelagic animals existed at mid-depths in the ocean (see also under *Oceana*). The net did not work properly, but after some modifications Fowler had two further and more successful trips on the *Research*, to the Faröe-Shetland Channel in 1897 under Usborne Moore and to the Bay of Biscay in 1900 under A.M. Field. During the 1900 cruise Fowler carried out one of the earliest attempts to study vertical migration of plankton in the surface layers.

References:
Bourne, 1889-90; Deacon, 1984; Fowler, 1896, 1898; Usborne Moore, 1899.

HMS RESEARCH

Survey vessel, launched Dartmouth 1939, 770 tons displacement, 142'6" waterline length, moulded beam 34', 160 b.h.p. diesel engine.

The vessel was to have been a brigantine-rigged non-magnetic vessel with auxiliary diesel power, devoted to the study of terrestrial magnetism and atmospheric electricity. The most extensive previous studies of these topics had been those conducted from the U.S. vessel *Carnegie*, belonging to the Department of Terrestrial Magnetism of the Carnegie Institute of Washington. Between 1909 and 1921 the *Carnegie* had undertaken six major cruises, but was then laid up for six years. In 1927 she was recommissioned for a proposed three-year cruise intended to occupy many of the stations worked during the earlier cruises. After spending most of 1928 in the Atlantic, and 1929 in the Pacific, the cruise came to an abrupt and tragic end when the vessel was destroyed by explosion and fire, killing the Captain, J.P. Ault, and a cabin boy during refuelling at Apia in Samoa.

The *Research* was intended to continue the work of the *Carnegie*, a plan enthusiastically supported by the American Geophysical Union. However, the outbreak of the Second World War intervened and the vessel was never completed, eventually simply being moved to Plymouth in 1952 to be broken up.

References:
Anon, 1935; Daily Telegraph and Morning Post, Monday October 17, 1938; Edgell, 1938.

RESOLUTION

Whitby whaler built 1803, part owned and commanded by William Scoresby Snr. William Scoresby Jnr. accompanied his father to the Greenland whale fishery each year in the *Resolution* from 1803 to 1810, and took command of the vessel himself in 1811 and 1812. Scoresby's oceanographic observations, which he continued in the *Esk* and the *Baffin*, began during these years in the *Resolution*. For more information see under *Esk*.

H.M.S. Rocket *photographed in 1924. Courtesy National Maritime Museum. Neg. no. N 2493.*

HMS ROCKET

"R" class destroyer, built 1916, c. 1,065 tons displacement, 265' long, 26'6" beam.
Used for physical oceanographic observations in the Bosphorus in 1922, in conjunction with
H.M.S. *H32.*

Reference:
Deacon, 1984.

ROSAURA

Private yacht belonging to Lord Moyne (the poet, novelist and playwright B.W. Guinness)
from which extensive biological samples were collected during a cruise in the North Atlantic in
1937-38.

The vessel had been built in 1905 as the cross-channel steamer *Dieppe,* 1552 tons gross, 700
tons registered, 282' long, powered by steam turbines. Prior to the 1937-38 voyage she was
converted to diesel power, but the lighting, heating and capstans were still powered by steam,
which was also used to drive the winch. The winch, carrying some 7,000m of wire, was that
fitted to the *Discovery* in 1923 for the Discovery Investigations and replaced by a more powerful
one for the B.A.N.Z.A.R. Expedition of 1929-31.

The voyage of the *Rosaura* was basically a pleasure cruise for Lord Moyne and a group of his
relatives and friends. However, the owner had an amateur interest in marine biology and
undertook to make collections for the British Museum (Natural History) under the supervision
of J.S. Colman.

The main plankton net was a 2m diameter stramin net without an opening/closing
mechanism, while benthic hauls were made with a 10' Agassiz trawl and 2' or 3' dredges. All
towed gears were fished from the bow with the ship going astern since the vessel was unable to
go ahead sufficiently slowly (see also *Research*).

128

The ship sailed from Southampton on 21 August 1937, under the command of H.M.S. Laidlaw and returned on 6 February 1938. She visited Greenland, sailed down the eastern seaboard of North America from Newfoundland to the Caribbean, thence along the north-east coast of South America to Pernambuco, crossed the Atlantic via St Paul's Rocks to Bathurst and returned to the U.K. via the Canaries.

In addition to shore collections at a variety of localities, some 60 hauls were made including plankton net samples to about 1300m and benthic samples to 1900m.

Publication of the results was held up by the outbreak of war, but a small number of reports appeared in the *Bulletin of the British Museum (Natural History)* in 1954, including the results of L.H.N. Cooper's examination of the transparency of water samples which Colman had collected from the Demerara and Barina Rivers. However, the collection was not, in general, considered to be particularly important and several of the groups have never been worked up.

In 1939 the *Rosaura* was hired by the Admiralty to be used as an armed boarding vessel and was sunk by a mine off Tobruk in 1941.

References:
Colman, 1954; Moyne, 1938.

HMS SALAMANDER

Wooden paddle sloop, built at Sheerness 1832, 818 (bm), 175'5" long, 31'10" beam, 220 n.h.p.

Salamander surveyed the Queensland coast and made hydrographic observations in 1866-67 under Capt. G.S. Nares who later commanded the *Challenger*. The vessel's initial task was to maintain links with the settlement at Somerset on Albany Pass, but surveying was added to her

H.M.S. Salamander, *from a sketch by R.S. Thomas. Courtesy National Maritime Museum. Neg. no. B 370.*

role when Nares was appointed to her, presumably because of his previous experience on the *Resolute.*

Salamander was ordered home in 1867 via Batavia and the Cape of Good Hope and Nares carried out a line of soundings during the passage through the Arafura Sea.

The *Salamander* was broken up in 1883.

Reference:
Deacon and Savours, 1976.

H.M.S. Samarang *undergoing repairs at Sarawak. Artist Richards. Courtesy National Maritime Museum. Neg. no. 9703.*

HMS SAMARANG

"Atholl" class 6th rate vessel, built at the Honourable East India Company yard in Cochin 1822, 500 (bm), 113'6" long, 32' beam.

After the end of hostilities in China in 1842 the *Samarang* was sent, under the command of Sir Edward Belcher (see also *Sulphur*), to survey the coasts of China, Japan, Korea and Borneo.   The voyage lasted from 1843-1846 and, in addition to the surveying work, Belcher made extensive marine collections and carried out a number of relatively deep soundings.

The *Samarang* was hulked as a guard-ship in 1837 at Gibraltar where she remained until she was broken up in 1883.

Reference:
Belcher, 1848.

SCOTIA

Barque-rigged, 400 ton auxiliary steam ship, 140' long, 29' beam, originally the Norwegian sealer / whaler *Hekla* used for the Danish expedition to the coast of Greenland under Lieut. C. Ryder in 1891-1892.

The *Hekla* was purchased in 1901 and renamed and refitted for the Scottish National

Antarctic Expedition of 1902-1904, inspired and led by William Spiers Bruce and sponsored by James and Andrew Coats.

Bruce had hoped to be able to obtain the *Balaena* in which he had visited the Antarctic in 1892-93 but the price demanded was exorbitant. Accordingly, he turned to Norway as a source for a suitable vessel and purchased the *Hekla* at Larvik for £2,620. The ship turned out to be in a far worse state than the pre-purchase survey had indicated and her repair and refitting in the Ailsa Shipbuilding Company yard at Troon cost some £8,000, including the fitting of new 55 h.p. engines built by Muir and Houston of Glasgow.

Scotia. *Courtesy Scott Polar Research Institute, Cambridge.*

During the expedition the *Scotia* was commanded by Capt. Thomas Robertson who had been in command of the *Active* on the *Balaena* Antarctic expedition. The main objective was a study of the Weddell Sea between Graham Land, the intended study area of the Swedish South Polar Expedition under Nordenskjöld from 1901 to 1904, and the mainland coast of Antarctica explored by Drygalski in the *Gauss* from 1901 to 1903.

The *Scotia* sailed to the Weddell Sea via the Falkland Islands and wintered during 1903 at Laurie Island in the South Orkneys. Here, a meteorological station was established and eventually handed over to the Argentine Government. It has been in continuous operation ever since. The ship returned to the Falklands for repairs and stores in November 1903 and thence to Buenos Aires where Bruce received confirmation of financial support for a further six months exploration. Accordingly, the *Scotia* returned to Laurie Island in February 1904, where the SNAE personnel were replaced by two Argentinians. The ship sailed southeastwards through the Weddell Sea to the Antarctic mainland where she was beset by ice for six days off what was named Coats Land before sailing north to Gough Island and thence via Cape Town, St Helena, Ascension Island and the Azores to the Clyde.

Throughout the voyage, and during the wintering period at Laurie Island, extensive meteorological, hydrographic, sounding and biological observations were made, fulfilling a more comprehensive programme than that of any previous or contemporary Antarctic expedition. Among the many important discoveries was the elimination of the "Ross Deep" where James Clark Ross had recorded a depth of more than 4000 fathoms (7320m) during the *Erebus* and *Terror* expedition of 1839-43. The *Scotia* recorded a depth of only 2,660 fathoms (4680m) some two miles away, corresponding fairly closely to the 2,200 fathoms attributed to Ross's sounding when the original figures were re-examined (see Deacon, 1971, Gould, 1924).

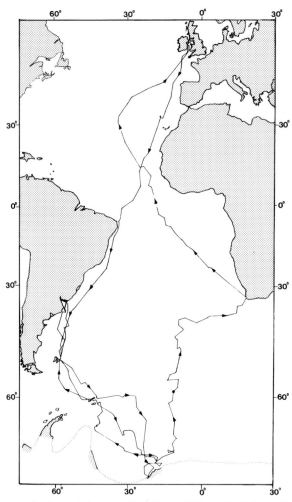

Track of the Scotia *during the Scottish National Antarctic Expedition, 1902-1904. Redrawn from Brown, Mossman and Pirie, 1906.*

After her return from the Antarctic, Bruce hoped that the *Scotia* would continue to be engaged in oceanographic work, ideally involved in training students from Scottish universities. Bruce's offer of the vessel to the Carnegie Trust for the Universities of Scotland elicited no response and the vessel was sold in 1905 to a Dundee whaling syndicate for £5,000. For some years she was employed in the Greenland whaling fishery under the command of Robertson, but by about 1910 she was laid up in Dundee along with numerous other whalers.

Following the loss of the *Titanic* in 1912 the *Scotia* was used for the first British contribution to the Atlantic Ice Patrol during 1913. The ship was again under the command of Thomas Robertson, but this time the scientific party was led by the hydrographer D.J. Matthews, then Assistant Director of the Marine Biological Association at Plymouth. Very extensive meteorological, hydrographic and biological observations were made during a total of some fifteen weeks at sea in the ice area of the north Atlantic.

Early in the First World War the vessel was sold once more and had a short career as a cargo vessel before she finally caught fire and was run ashore on the Isles of Scilly where she burnt out.

References:
Bernstein, 1985; Brown, 1923; Brown, Mossman and Pirie, 1906; Matthews, Taylor and Crawshay, 1914.

HMS SEALARK

Composite screw survey vessel, 1-3 pdr, built Greenwich 1878, 900 tons displacement, 185'6" long, 29' beam, 500 i.h.p., purchased in 1903 and used for the Percy Sladen Trust Expedition to the Indian Ocean in 1905.

The vessel was named *Wanderer* originally, but at the time of purchase by the Admiralty was named *Consuelo*. After purchase she was initially named *Investigator* and renamed *Sealark* in January 1904. Originally the vessel was square-rigged, but she was refitted with fore and aft sails for her naval service.

Gardiner and Forster Cooper, who eventually formed the civilian scientific party on the *Sealark,* had both visited the Laccadive and Maldive Islands in 1899-1900 to investigate the coral faunas. Gardiner, then a Demonstrator in Animal Morphology at Cambridge, had been encouraged to continue and extend this work and in 1904 approached the Royal Society for support in organizing a major expedition to the Indian Ocean. The main argument for such an expedition was that the biology of the region was very poorly known since it had been missed by the *Challenger* and very little had been carried out subsequently other than by the *Valdivia* and the *Investigator.*

Gardiner hoped that the Government of India would provide support for the venture, but this was not forthcoming. Eventually, after an approach by the Royal Society, the British Admiralty placed the *Sealark* at his disposal, under the Command of Cdr. H. Boyle Townshend Somerville, and agreed to bear all the expenses of the vessel itself. To cover the costs of the equipment and of the subsequent sorting of the catches, the British Association provided £150, the Francis Maitland Balfour memorial fund at Cambridge a further £350 and the Percy Sladen Trust covered the remaining costs. This latter fund had been established in 1904 with a £20,000 endowment by Sladen's widow in memory of her husband, a wealthy amateur naturalist who had died in 1900. Sladen had published extensively on the echinoderms, including the reports on the starfishes collected from the *Challenger, Knight Errant* and *Triton.*

The principal objective of Gardiner's proposed expedition was to seek evidence for past land bridges in the Indian Ocean region, and particularly between Madagascar and India, mainly by a study of the terrestrial faunas of the various islands and their neighbouring marine faunas. In addition, however, extensive topographical and physical and chemical oceanographic observations were to be made and mid-water samples collected. Accordingly, apart from triangular and rectangular dredges and Agassiz trawls, the *Sealark* also carried vertical and horizontal opening / closing townets (see also under *Silver Belle*), Negretti and Zambra maximum / minimum and Richter's reversing thermometers, Lucas sounding machines and snapper leads, and an Ekman current meter. The ship was supposed to have been fitted with a 2000 fathom main dredging wire in Ceylon before the expedition began. In fact, the wire did not reach the ship until she visited Mauritius, half way through the cruise, so that the limited deep sea work was restricted to the second half of the expedition.

The *Sealark* sailed from Colombo on May 9 1905, making first for the Chagos Archipelago and finding no evidence of a shallow ridge between this group and the Maldives to the north. In the Chagos group extensive collecting and surveying work was carried out at Salomon, Peros Banhos, Diego Garcia and Egmont Atolls.

H.M.S. Sealark *photographed in 1904. Courtesy National Maritime Museum. Neg. no. N 10560.*

The vessel now made for Mauritius, sounding regularly during the passage but finding no evidence of the southern extension of the mid Indian Ocean ridge eventually discovered by echo-sounder during the voyage of the *Dana* in 1930 and later surveyed by the *Mabahiss* in 1933-34.

After further extensive collecting and surveying at Mauritius, the vessel moved north to investigate Cargados Carajos and the Saya de Malha Bank before arriving at the Seychelles on September 10. A total of 12 days was spent collecting here, rather more than expected since the ship's engine had to be dismantled to repair a bent piston rod.

From the Seychelles the *Sealark* went to Farquhar, Providence and St Pierce Islands, obtaining manganese nodules in the deepest dredge haul of the expedition, at 744 fathoms (1360m) off Providence Island.

After a short call at the Amirante Islands the vessel returned to the Seychelles for more collecting and surveying on various islands in the group until December 8 when Gardiner and Forster Cooper caught a mail steamer back to England.

Apart from the very extensive terrestrial and coastal collections, almost 200 dredge hauls were made, mostly in very shallow waters but three in depths greater than 500 fathoms (915m). Much of the shallow water dredging work was conducted from the *Sealark's* launch *Xanthus* which had been purchased at Colombo. Some 60 major townet hauls were made, again mostly in shallow depths, but with a few much deeper hauls down to 1200 fathoms (2195m). In connection with the extensive sounding work, 45 good seabed samples were obtained in depths down to about 2450 fathoms (4481m). Finally, 26 sets of serial temperature observations were made together with 29 measurements of the near bottom temperature.

The results of the expedition were published under Gardiner's editorship in the Transactions of the Linnean Society between 1907 and 1926. Most of these reports dealt exclusively with the Percy Sladen Expedition material, but several included data from other sources. In particular, the report of D.J. Matthews on the physical oceanographic data incorporated the results of extensive collections of surface temperatures and water samples by 21 merchant vessels and the Austrian cruiser *Panther* covering areas of the western Indian Ocean not visited by the *Sealark*. The merchant vessels were already keeping meteorological logs and the collection of the additional data was arranged for Matthews by Cdr. M.W. Campbell-Hepworth, then Marine Superintendent of the Meteorological Office.

References:
Gardiner and Forster Cooper, 1907; Matthews, 1926.

HMS SHEARWATER

Wooden paddle packet, 343 (bm), 137′ long, 23′ beam, previously the Post Office vessel *Dolphin* built at Harwich in 1826 and transferred to the Navy in 1837.

The *Shearwater* was fitted out as a survey vessel at Woolwich in 1841 at a cost of £5,673. She became the principal vessel used for surveys in U.K. waters during the 1840s under Capt. J. Washington and Cdr. C.G. Robinson until she was diverted to relieve the famine in western Ireland in 1848. The *Shearwater* had replaced the *Fairy* after the latter had been lost in 1840 and Washington continued the tidal observations in the North Sea made by the *Fairy's* captain, William Hewett. In 1842 Washington confirmed Hewett's earlier report of an amphidromal point, with little or no tidal rise and fall, in the southern North Sea.

The *Shearwater's* surveying role was eventually taken over by the *Porcupine* from 1856 and she was sold at Malta in 1857 for £1,025.

References:
Day, 1967; Deacon, 1971; Washington, 1842.

HMS SHEARWATER

Wooden screw sloop, 4-64 pdr, built Pembroke Dock 1861, 669 (bm), 913 tons displacement, 160′ long, 30′ beam, 532 i.h.p., 150 n.h.p., complement 130.

The *Shearwater,* under the command of Capt. G.S. Nares, was made available to W.B. Carpenter for a survey in the Straits of Gibraltar in 1871 on her way to the Red Sea. As a result of the temperature observations made during the cruise of the *Lightning* in 1868, Carpenter had postulated that oceanic deep currents were due to density differences rather than being wind-driven. He therefore hoped that the demonstration of an outflowing undercurrent through the Straits due to density differences between Atlantic and Mediterranean waters would prove this case. Observations carried out from H.M.S. *Porcupine* during the summer of 1870 strongly suggested that such an outflow existed, but Carpenter hoped for further evidence to counter criticisms of his ideas.

New observations of salinity and temperature were made in the Straits during August 1871 and the sub-surface currents were followed with current drogues consisting of four vertical canvas fins stretched between iron bars and suspended from a buoy or small boat. The ability to recognise the outflowing Mediterranean water by its relatively high salinity supported Carpenter's case, though he accepted that more work would be required to reach a complete understanding of the exchange of water between the Mediterranean and the Atlantic (Carpenter, 1872).

After the work in the Straits the *Shearwater* proceeded to the Red Sea. During the passage

H.M.S. Shearwater *(1861). Reproduced by permission of the Hydrographer to the Navy.*

through the Mediterranean further physical and biological observations were made. From the results of limited dredging between Sicily and the coast of North Africa, Carpenter came to the conclusion that "in the Mediterranean Basin the existence of Animal life in any abundance at a depth greater than 200 fathoms will be found quite exceptional. . . Thus it appears that Edward Forbes was quite justified in the conclusion he drew *as regards the particular locality he had investigated;* and that his only mistake lay in supposing that the same conclusions would prevail in the open Ocean."

Nares returned to England in 1872 to take command of H.M.S. *Challenger,* taking with him Lieut. T.H. Tizard and Lieut. G.R. Bethell. Cdr. W.J.L. Wharton took Nares' place in the *Shearwater* and surveyed in the Mediterranean and off the east coast of Africa from 1872 to 1875, including observations of the transit of Venus in 1874.

The *Shearwater* was broken up in 1877.

References:
Day, 1967; Deacon, 1971.

SILVER BELLE

North Sea fishing ketch built Grimsby 1886, 130 tons gross, 77' long, 21' beam, owned by R. Norris Wolfenden and refitted as a yacht with a steam capstan and used to replace the much smaller *Walwin* from 1902.

Between 1903 and 1907 Wolfenden conducted a series of expeditions, with his skipper Buchan Henry, in the north-eastern Atlantic between the British Isles and the Azores, Madeira and Gibraltar, in the Faröe-Shetland Channel and between the Hebrides, Shetland and Norway. During these expeditions, and the earlier cruises in the *Walwin,* many hydrographic stations were worked and the results were reported by H.N. Dickson in appendices to Wolfenden's general account of his oceanographic work published by the Challenger Society in 1909. The observations were particularly valuable because they provided data from areas extending well beyond those covered by the investigations organized from 1902 by the International Council for the Exploration of the Sea.

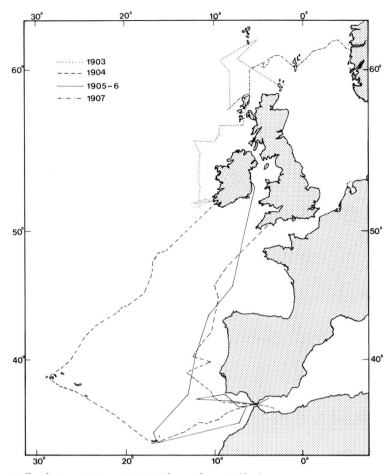

Tracks of the Silver Belle *during 1903 to 1907. Redrawn from Wolfenden, 1909.*

In addition, more than 400 plankton hauls were obtained at depths ranging from 50 to 2000 fathoms (92 to 3658m). For most of these Wolfenden used his own design of opening / closing horizontally hauled plankton net, but during 1903, in the Faröe-Shetland Channel, he also used the vertical net designed by G.H. Fowler and used from the *Research.* Both types of net were employed by J. Stanley Gardiner during the Percy Sladen Trust Expedition to the Indian Ocean in the *Sealark* in 1905.

A relatively small number of benthic samples were obtained down to depths of about 500 fathoms (915m) with Agassiz trawls, beam trawls, otter trawls and dredges.

Wolfenden's account of the cruises was accompanied by restricted reports on the biological collections by E.W.L. Holt and L.W. Byrne (fishes), W.H. Tattersall (amphipods and isopods), and G.P. Farran (the genus *Pyrosoma*).

Reference:
Wolfenden, 1909.

SOUTHERN CROSS

Norwegian wooden sealing barque, originally named *Pollux,* built at Arendal, Norway 1886, 146'6" long, 30'6" beam, 522 tons gross, 277 tons net, designed by Colin Archer who had also designed Nansen's ship, the *Fram.*

The *Pollux* was purchased in 1898 by Carsten Egeberg Borchgrevink and renamed *Southern Cross* for an antarctic expedition in which he planned to make the first intentional overwintering on the Antarctic mainland. In preparation for the voyage the ship was fitted with 100 registered horse power vertical expansion engines built by I. and A. Jensen of Dahl, Frederikstad, Norway. This work was to have been done in England, but an engineering strike made this impossible.

Borchgrevink, a childhood friend of Roald Amundsen, had failed to obtain financial backing for his expedition in his native Norway. He therefore came to London and eventually obtained some £38,000 from the publisher Sir George Newnes, on the understanding that the vessel should sail under the British flag. Accordingly, Borchgrevink took three British subjects, William Colbeck who sailed as extra master, magnetic observer and cartographer, Louis Bernacchi an Australian physicist who later sailed on the *Discovery,* and Hugh Blackwall Evans who sailed as assistant zoologist and eventually far outlived his antarctic contemporaries to die in Canada in 1975 at the age of 100. Otherwise, however, the members of the Expedition were virtually all Norwegian, including Bernhard Jensen, the sailing master, and Nicolai Hanson, the zoologist who died at Cape Adare in October 1899, apparently of beriberi.

The *Southern Cross* left England in August 1898 and, after calling at Madeira and St Vincent, reached Hobart, Tasmania on 28 November, sailing once more on 19 December. The vessel spent 43 days beset by the pack ice but eventually got through and reached Cape Adare on 17 February 1899 Having landed the shore party, consisting of Borchgrevink and nine companions, she left again on March 1 to spend the southern winter in Australian waters and returned to Cape Adare on 28 January 1900. After collecting the shore party, excluding Hanson of course, the *Southern Cross* sailed on 2 February. She ran along some 400 miles of the Ross Ice Barrier and landed sledge parties which held the farthest south record until this was exceeded by Scott from the *Discovery.* The homeward voyage via the Auckland Islands was very stormy but the vessel eventually reached Melbourne in April 1900. From here, the scientific staff returned home in R.M.S. *Ortona,* arriving in England in June 1900.

The oceanographic results of the expedition were extremely limited, being restricted to a small number of sub-surface temperature measurements, apparently taken with thermometers supplied by Negretti and Zambra, and a few deep soundings, including some near the Ice Barrier. During the stay at Cape Adare the shore party made extensive meteorological and magnetic observations and collected biological and geological samples including some dredged from shallow water. However, these collections were rather disappointing, partly because they were so limited, but also because many were badly preserved and poorly documented. Consequently, the official reports on the collections, published by the Natural History Museum and edited by R. Bowdler Sharpe and F. Jeffrey Bell, contain critical comments. Much of the rsponsibility, particularly for the lack of adequate documentation, seems to be attributable to Borchgrevink who appears to have lost, or suppressed, several of the notebooks and journals which he received from expedition members as well as some of the collections.

After the Expedition the *Southern Cross* was bought by the Newfoundland Sealing Company and was eventually lost with all hands off the Newfoundland Coast.

References:
Bernacchi, 1901; Borchgrevink, 1900, 1901; Evans, 1974; Evans and Jones, 1974; Jones, 1975; Sharpe and Bell, 1902

HMS SPITFIRE

Wooden paddle gunvessel, 5 guns, built at Deptford 1845, 432 (bm), 595 tons displacement, 147′ long, 25′ beam, 140 n.h.p.

The *Spitfire* became a survey vessel in 1851 and from this time until 1856 was under the command of T.A.B. Spratt surveying in the Mediterranean. From 1851 to 1853 Spratt worked around Crete carrying out surveying and archaeological work, the two studies elucidating the changes in the relative levels of land and sea which had occurred in historical times.

The Crete survey was interrupted by the Crimea War from 1854 and the *Spitfire* became fully engaged in surveying work connected with the hostilities. Although his surveys were therefore confined to shallow inshore waters, Spratt did not lose his scientific interests, aroused dring his service on the *Beacon* under Thomas Graves and particularly during Edward Forbes' period on the ship. During the 1850s a great deal of deep-sea sounding work was being carried out to survey routes for submarine telegraph cables (see, for instance, *Cyclops* and *Gorgon*). Spratt's blacksmith on the *Spitfire,* Carmelo Bonnici, devised a sounding instrument, Bonnici's claw, to release the weight necessary to carry down the sounding line from the sediment sampler which had to be retrieved. Spratt had great confidence in the new instrument, but found it to be disappointingly unreliable when he came to use it in deep water in his next command, the *Medina.*

The vessel became a tug in 1861 and was broken up at Bermuda in 1888.

References:

Deacon, 1978; McConnell, 1982

H.M.S. Stork. *Courtesy Imperial War Museum. Neg. no. Q 40857.*

HMS STORK

Wooden composite screw gunboat, 2-64 pdr, 2-20 pdr, built Poplar 1882, 465 tons, 125' long, 23'6" beam, 360 i.h.p., complement 60.

The *Stork* was commissioned as a survey vessel in 1888 and was employed mainly in the Indian Ocean and south-western Pacific until she was lent as a training ship in 1913. During 1898, under the command of Cdr. H.J. Gedge, the *Stork* was used for current measurements in the Straits of Bab-el-Mandeb between the Red Sea and the Gulf of Aden. Gedge recorded a surface current flowing into the Red Sea and one in the opposite direction at a depth of about 100 fathoms (180m). These observations were made using a Pillsbury current meter, apparently only the third set of naval measurements with the instrument since the Admiralty had acquired it in 1896 (see also under *Research* and *Egeria*).

The *Stork* was broken up in 1950 at Lower Rainham, Kent, and her hull was used as a wharf.

References:
Deacon, 1971; Gedge, 1898; McConnell, 1982; Wharton, 1898.

HMS SULPHUR

"Hecla" class bomb vessel, 1-13″ mortar, 1-10″ mortar, 2-6 pdr, 8-24 pdr, built Chatham Dockyard 1826, 372 (bm), 105′ long, 28′6″ beam, design complement 67.

In 1828 the *Sulphur* was employed as an emigrant ship to New Holland (Australia).

From December 1835 to July 1842 the vessel was sent for surveying work and scientific enquiry around the Pacific Islands. She was initially under the command of Capt. F.W. Beechey, but he became ill and had to return to England from Valparaiso when Lt. Cdr. Henry Kellett took command until Edward Belcher joined the ship in Panama. Belcher was interested in malacology and probably this contributed to the fact that, in addition to the land collections, extensive dredging was carried out in shallow water. Ultimately the *Sulphur's* surgeon-naturalist, Richard Brinsley Hinds, edited the superbly illustrated zoological results of the voyage.

On her return from the Pacific the *Sulphur* was transferred to harbour duty, being hulked at Woolwich in 1843 as a receiving ship, and was broken up in 1857, by which time she was the last bomb vessel on the navy list.

References:
Hinds, 1844; Ritchie, 1967.

HMS TARTARUS

Paddle gunvessel, 2-9 pdr, built Pembroke Dock 1834, 523 (bm), 145′ long, 28′4″ beam, originally 100 n.h.p., re-engined in 1837 with 136 n.h.p. engines.

In 1857 the *Tartarus* was used to survey the route for a telegraph cable from Crete to Alexandria under the command of Cdr. Arthur Lakis Mansell. Mansell used a variety of sounding instruments including modifications of the Brooke sounder and Bonnici's claws, the latter developed on the *Spitfire*. Finally, Mansell's Master, Francis Skead, produced a one-armed version of Bonnici's claw.

When the cable was laid in 1858-59 three unsuccessful attempts were made and more than 800 miles of cable were lost (Deacon, 1978). This seemed to be partly because the cable was faulty, but partly because the route chosen, through the deep eastern basin of the Mediterranean, was unsuitable. Consequently, when the Malta to Alexandria cable was laid in

1861 the route chosen, and surveyed by Spratt in the *Medina,* avoided the deep basin by crossing to Tripoli and then following the North African coast.

The *Tartarus* was broken up at Malta in 1860.

References:

Deacon, 1978; Mansell, 1857; McConnell, 1982.

TERRA NOVA

Steam powered wooden barque built 1884 by Alexander Stephen and Sons, Dundee, 743 tons gross, 150 tons net, 187′ long, 31′ beam, compound vertical engine, 140 n.h.p. The *Terra Nova* was the last whaler built in Dundee.

The vessel was operated in the Newfoundland sealing trade from 1884 to 1903, initially under the ownership of the builders, sold to David Bruce in 1893 and then to C.T. Bowring and Company of St Johns in 1898.

In 1903 the *Terra Nova* was hired by the Admiralty to accompany the *Morning* to relieve Scott in the *Discovery* which had been located ice-bound in McMurdo Sound by the *Morning* the previous season. She was hurriedly refitted and re-rigged in Dundee under the supervision of Vice Admiral Pelham Aldrich who had sailed with Nares on the *Challenger* and the *Alert* and had recently retired. Her loading with stores and coal was supervised by Ernest Shackleton who had been invalided home from the National Antarctic Expedition and had returned to England on the *Morning.*

The *Terra Nova* left Dundee under the command of H. Mackay on 21 August 1903 and, after

Terra Nova. *Courtesy National Maritime Museum. Neg. no. G 5507.*

calling at Portland, was towed by a succession of naval ships to Gibraltar and then through the Mediterranean and into the Indian Ocean in order to save both time and coal. She arrived in Hobart, Tasmania, on 31 October, in good time to transfer stores to the *Morning.*

The two vessels sailed on 6 December and reached the *Discovery* on 5 January 1904 after a difficult passage through the Southern Ocean. The *Discovery* was still ice-bound and Scott made arrangements for the Expedition personnel to be taken off by the two relief ships if this should become necessary. However, on 16 February, after several abortive attempts to blast or saw *Discovery* free, she was released and the three ships sailed north on 19th. They took separate routes to the Auckland Islands and then sailed to Lyttelton, New Zealand, arriving on April 1, 1904.

After being dry docked for caulking and cleaning, the *Terra Nova* sailed for England via the Falklands, arriving at Sheerness on 18 August, a month ahead of the *Discovery.*

In 1904 the *Terra Nova* was sent to Franz Joseph Land to relieve the U.S. expedition under W. Ziegler in the *America,* also a Dundee built vessel, previously the *Esquimaux.*

In 1906 she returned to the Newfoundland sealing trade until November 1909 when she was purchased for her most famous role, Scott's British Antarctic Expedition of 1910 to 1913 which ended in the epic journey to the South Pole and the tragic death of Scott and his four companions. Scott would have preferred his old ship, *Discovery,* but when this proved impossible he took the *Terra Nova* as a second choice.

The expedition was financed partly by private funds, including the fees of two paying volunteers, and partly by a grant of £20,000 from the Government and with the *Terra Nova* crewed largely by naval personnel. The ship was registered as a yacht in Scott's name to avoid the necessity to conform to merchant shipping regulations and, since Scott was elected a member of the Royal Yacht Squadron, she was able to sail under the white ensign.

The *Terra Nova* left the U.K. in June 1910, under the command of Lieut. E.R.G. Evans. After calling at Cape Town, where Scott rejoined her and took command, she sailed on to Australia and then to Lyttelton, New Zealand, where she stayed for a month, finally leaving for the Antarctic on 29 November. She entered the pack ice on 9 December and spent 20 days passing through it, reaching Cape Evans on Ross Island, the site of the southern base, on 4 January 1911. Having landed the shore party, including Scott and Evans, *Terra Nova* sailed once more on 26 January, now under the command of Lieut. Victor L.A. Campbell. The intention was to sail eastward, along the Ice Barrier, to King Edward VII Land and to establish a second shore base near Cape Colbeck. Ice conditions made this impossible so Campbell sailed into the Bay of Whales as an alternative site for the base, but found the *Fram* and Amundsen's base already established here. He returned therefore to Cape Evans to give Scott the news and eventually established his own base at Cape Adare on Victoria Land, where Borchgrevink had wintered during the *Southern Cross* Expedition in 1899.

After leaving Cape Adare on 20 February, now under the command of Cdr. H.L.L. Pennell, the *Terra Nova* was to attempt to survey the coast to the west of North Cape, an area previously unexplored. Although ice conditions were not good, two short lengths of coastline were seen and named Oates Land before the ship had to move off northwards. After a difficult voyage, largely against head winds, she reached Lyttelton on 1 April.

During the outward voyage from England, townet samples had been taken whenever possible under the supervision of Dennis G. Lillie who had responsibility for all of the shipboard biological work. Soundings also had been taken with a Lucas sounding machine, particularly in the Ross Sea, under the supervision of Lieut. Henry E. de P. Rennick.

From July to October 1911, after a three month refit at Lyttelton, the *Terra Nova* carried out an extensive survey around the Three Kings Islands and between this group and the North Cape of New Zealand. Soundings were taken routinely during the day, the sounding machine being powered by a modified motor-boat engine. Biological sampling was carried out during the night, a total of some 80 plankton hauls being made, together with seven trawl and dredge hauls at depths between 15 and 300 fathoms (28-548m). On the way back to Lyttelton, Lillie was landed at Whangamumu, near the Bay of Islands, to spend a month working on the factory ships of the New Zealand Whaling Company and collecting extensive biological material. During the second winter he was to spend a further four months at Whangamumu.

After two months at Lyttelton the ship sailed on December 15 1911 and relieved the shore parties with considerable difficulty. During this voyage, townetting, trawling and sounding were carried out whenever the opportunity presented itself and particularly during the week or so the ship was in the pack ice. The vessel returned to Lyttelton on 2 April 1912 to be greeted by the news of Amundsen's successful expedition to the South Pole.

During the 1912 winter the *Terra Nova* was again refitted and from June to October a surveying party worked in Admiralty Bay from motor launches, using the ship's Lucas sounding machine.

The ship left Lyttelton to relieve the shore bases on 14 December 1912 with the intention of running a line of soundings from Banks Peninsula to 60°S: 170°W and then of proceeding south to pass through the pack ice as close as possible to 165°W, that is rather more to the west than previous expeditions through the Ross Sea. The weather was in general very good, although the extent of the ice was much greater than previously experienced. An extensive scientific programme was conducted including townetting, trawling, sounding and water sampling with Nansen-Pettersson insulating water bottles.

Cape Evans was reached on 18 January 1913 and the tragic news of the loss of Scott's Southern Party during the previous season was received.

After collecting geological specimens left by various of the land sledge parties and depositing provisions for any future explorers, the ship began her return journey to New Zealand on 26 January, reaching Lyttelton on 12 February having continued the scientific work throughout the voyage.

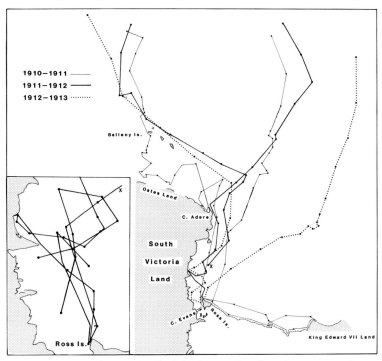

Tracks of the Terra Nova *1910-1913 with, inset, details of the ship's tracks off South Victoria Land in January to March 1912. Redrawn from Huxley, 1913. It is not possible to reconcile the dates on the published version of the inset section with the narratives by Evans and Pennell. I have therefore omitted these dates and simply give the undifferentiated tracks.*

On March 13 the *Terra Nova* left New Zealand on her homeward voyage, sailing east at about 59°S until Cape Horn was cleared and then sailing north via Rio de Janeiro and the Azores to reach Cardiff on 14 June 1913.

During the two voyages between England and New Zealand a total of about 70 plankton samples were obtained and during the homeward journey two trawl hauls were taken, one on the Falkland Shelf and one off Rio. In addition to the samples obtained during the winter cruise around the Three Kings Islands, a further 135 plankton tows were made between New Zealand and McMurdo Sound and 15 trawl hauls, from depths between 40 and 300 fathoms (73 to 548m) were obtained in the Ross Sea, together with about 50 sediment samples taken with the sounding tube.

Marine work at Cape Evans consisted mainly of the collection of townet samples through holes cut in the sea ice, and temperature measurements using Richter reversing thermometers and Nansen-Pettersson water bottles. Water samples were collected for subsequent salinity determinations.

A summary of the scientific results appeared in *Scott's Last Expedition* (1913), edited by Leonard Huxley, and the detailed natural history results were published by the British Museum (Natural History) in a series of reports which appeared between 1914 and 1935. This series was financed partly by £6,000 allocated for the purpose from the fund raised by public subscription after the return of the expedition.

A further £11,500 was allocated for the preparation of the meteorological, glaciological and physiographical results to be published under the supervision of a committee of which H.G. Lyons was the chairman. The First World War delayed these reports, but they appeared eventually between 1919 and 1924. The last volume in this series contains a large amount of miscellaneous data about the expedition, compiled by Lyons, making this one of the best documented expeditions ever to leave British shores.

The detailed temperature observations made by E.W. Nelson at Cape Evans, and the salinity observations on his water samples apparently made by D.J. Matthews at the Plymouth laboratory, were never published. However, the data were examined by Deacon (1975) and evaluated in the light of later observations in the same region.

Following her antarctic voyages, the *Terra Nova* returned to the Newfoundland seal industry for many years under the ownership of C.T. Bowring and Company of St. Johns. Eventually she was sunk by enemy action off Newfoundland in 1943.

References:
Deacon, 1975; Huxley, 1913; Jones, 1972b, 1973; Lyons, 1924.

HMS TERROR

"Vesuvius" class bomb vessel, guns as *Erebus,* built Topsham 1813, 325 (bm), 102′ long, 27′ beam, design complement 67. Used for the antarctic voyage of James Clark Ross in the *Erebus,* 1839-1843, the *Terror* being commanded by Francis R.M. Crozier and with Archibald McMurdo as First Lieutenant (for details, see under *Erebus*).

The *Terror* had participated in the American War of 1815 but had then been laid up in ordinary until 1828 when she was sent to the Mediterranean to be used against the Barbary Pirates. She never reached the Mediterranean since she was wrecked near Lisbon, salvaged and returned to Plymouth for repair. The vessel was commissioned in 1836 for George Back's Arctic voyage in which he intended to winter in the neighbourhood of Repulse Bay and to extend the recent land explorations. In the event, Back never reached Repulse Bay. The *Terror* became ice-bound in September 1836 and was not released until July 1837 after which she limped back to the United Kingdom, being beached in a near sinking condition at Lough Swilly in Ireland.

After the antarctic voyage the *Erebus* and *Terror* were used during Sir John Franklin's ill-fated Arctic expedition of 1845, the *Terror* being commanded once more by Francis Crozier. In preparation for the Arctic expedition both vessels had been fitted with retractable screws and with modified locomotive steam engines to provide auxiliary power to the main propulsion which remained the sails. Crozier took over command of the expedition after Franklin's death in 1847 and abandoned the two ships, beset by ice off King William Island, in April 1848.

References:
Back, 1838; Day, 1967; Lloyd, 1970.

HMS THALIA

"Leda" class frigate, 46 guns, ordered from Portsmouth but ultimately built Chatham Dockyard 1830, 1053 (bm), 150'1.5" long, 39'9" beam, design complement 284.

Capt. Robert Wauchope, in command of the *Thalia* in 1836, collected a water sample from a depth of 635 fathoms (1161m) close to the equator off the Gulf of Guinea and measured its temperature and salinity.

Wauchope had had a long standing interest in scientific matters going back to at least 1816 when he had attempted to measure deep temperatures from the *Eurydice.*

The *Thalia* was employed in harbour duties in 1855, being hulked at Portsmouth as a chapel ship. She was broken up in 1867. H.M.S. *Unicorn,* an almost identical vessel belonging to the same class, is in the process of restoration at Dundee.

References:
Deacon, 1971; Wauchope, 1836-39.

HMS TRINCULO

"Cruizer" class brig sloop, 389 (bm), built by Tyson at Bursledon, 1809.

Edward Massey sailed on the *Trinculo* in 1832, under the command of James R. Booth, to test three new types of sounding apparatus. The results were reported originally in the *Cork Reporter* and the article was reprinted in *Nautical Magazine,* vol. 1, 498-499.

The *Trinculo* had been converted to a ship sloop in 1828 and back to a brig sloop in 1832. She was broken up in 1841.

References:
Deacon, 1971; McConnell, 1982

HMS TRITON

Composite paddle steamer, built Poplar 1882, 410 tons displacement, 370 i.h.p. Built to replace the *Porcupine* as the principal survey vessel in home waters.

The *Triton* was commissioned by T.H. Tizard in May 1882 and was made available during August and September that year for an investigation of the Faröe-Shetland Channel to extend the work on the Wyville Thomson Ridge carried out during the cruise of the *Knight Errant* in

H.M.S. Triton. *Courtesy National Maritime Museum. Neg. no. 4077.*

1880. Originally the cruise had been proposed by Wyville Thomson, but the request had been refused. Thomson had died in March 1882 and John Murray, who had succeeded him as head of the *Challenger* office, had re-applied successfully. Extensive sounding, submarine temperature measurements, tow-netting and trawling work was carried out around the Wyville Thomson Ridge, the results of the zoological work being published largely in the *Proceedings of the Royal Society of Edinburgh.*

H.M.S. Triton. *Photographed at Gravesend in 1961 when she was up for sale. Courtesy National Maritime Museum. Neg. no. A 2659C.*

146

This was the last of a series of scientific cruises on naval ships with civilian oceanographers which began with the *Lightning* cruise in 1868. British scientists had little further opportunity to work in the deep sea environment until the establishment of the *Discovery* Investigations in the 1920s.

The *Triton* was used extensively for surveying work in British waters until she was decommissioned in 1914 along with the *Research,* the last paddle vessels to be used by the Hydrographic Department. The *Triton* was assigned to harbour duties during the war and was used as a cadet training ship at Gravesend between the wars. She was sold in 1961 and towed to Bruges to be broken up. According to Day (1967) her hull was still sound after lying in the West India Docks for 42 years!

References:
Deacon, 1977; Tizard, 1883.

HMS VALOROUS

"Magicienne" class wooden paddle frigate, built Pembroke Dock 1851, 1257 (bm), 2045 tons displacement, 210′ long, 36′ beam, 1145 i.h.p., 400 n.h.p. The *Valorous* was the last paddle frigate built for the Navy; by the time she was sold in 1891 she had outlived all of the others, most of them by at least 20 years.

In the summer of 1875 the *Valorous* was employed, under the command of Capt. Loftus F. Jones, as a supply vessel for the Arctic Expedition in the *Alert* and *Discovery* to carry coal and stores as far as Disco Island off the west coast of Greenland. The supply vessel was originally to have been a merchant ship, but once the decision had been made to use a man-o-war instead, the Royal Society, at the suggestion of W.B. Carpenter, approached the Admiralty for permission to make oceanographic observations during the return voyage to fill in a major gap left by the *Challenger* Expedition, then in progress.

H.M.S. Valorous. *Courtesy National Maritime Museum. Neg. no. 6845.*

The scientific work was undertaken by J. Gwyn Jeffreys with the assistance of Carpenter's son who had accompanied his father on the *Lightning* in 1868. A grant of £120 was made from the Royal Society Donation Fund to cover the scientists' costs, including "certain messing expenses" which they were expected to pay (see Jeffreys, 1877), reflecting, perhaps, the parsimony of the Treasury which later threatened the publication of the *Challenger* Reports.

Valorous left Spithead on 29 May and reached Disco on 6 July. On the outward voyage the vessel was to sail directly to Disco, with no delays for scientific work. Nevertheless, a few surface townet samples were obtained in the intervals between the severe storms which were encountered, and during the stay at Godhavn, where the coal and stores were transferred to the *Alert* and *Discovery*, Jeffreys obtained several shallow dredge samples from one of the ship's cutters.

Having transferred all the stores and collected Clements Markham who had travelled out in the *Alert* with his cousin Cdr. A.H. Markham, the *Valorous* made the return voyage, occupying 16 major stations, nine of them in depths greater than 1000 fathoms, the last and deepest being at 1785 fathoms (3265m) at 55°10′N: 25°58′W. Bad weather prevented any further scientific work and *Valorous* docked on 29 August.

Station 13, at about 56°N: 34°42′W, was much shallower (690 fathoms, 1256m) than the stations on either side. This sounding was on what is now known to be the Reykjanes Ridge on which M'Clintock had recorded a similarly shallow sounding from the *Bulldog* in 1860 and which Wallich (1861) had identified as the "sunken land of Buss".

Successful dredge hauls were obtained at most of the stations, and at four of them serial temperature measurements were made between the surface and the bottom. W.B. Carpenter had intended that subsurface water samples would be collected and had obtained two Buchanan stop-cock water-bottles (see McConnell, 1982) for his son's use. However, Nares persuaded Carpenter to allow one of these bottles to be transferred to the *Alert* which had not been supplied with water bottles by the Admiralty. The bottle remaining on the *Valorous* failed to work, having a defect also experienced in the similar bottles supplied to the *Challenger,* so that no sub-surface water samples were collected and specific gravity determinations were restricted to surface samples.

The temperature results were reported and discussed by W.B. Carpenter (1876) in terms of his ideas of a general oceanic circulation driven by density differences caused by temperature variations, originally prompted by the results obtained on the *Lightning.* He expressed the

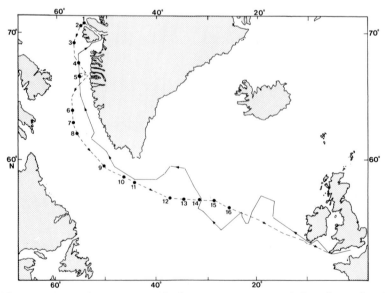

Track of H.M.S. Valorous, *May to August 1875, with the station positions marked. Redrawn from Jeffreys, 1876.*

hope that the temperature sections between Iceland and Greenland, and across Davis Strait, which the *Valorous* was unable to make, would be completed the following year by the vessel which was to be sent to communicate with the *Alert* and *Discovery*. In the event, this was not achieved because of the curtailment of the Arctic Expedition following the outbreak of scurvy (see *Alert*).

The biological results were reported by Jeffreys (1876), who concentrated on his own special interest, the molluscs, and by A.M. Norman, W.C. M'Intosh, G.J. Allman, P.M. Duncan, W.B. Carpenter and G. Dickie who each appended short reports on other groups collected. Most of the material found its way to the British Museum thus fulfilling a condition of the support of the Admiralty, but Jeffreys was able to keep many of the molluscs in his private collection which eventually went to the Smithsonian Institution in Washington.

References:
Bartsch, Rehder and Shields, 1946; Carpenter, 1876; Jeffreys, 1876; Laing, 1980; Mills, 1978; Osbon, 1982.

WALWIN

Sailing cutter, built at Salcombe 1883, 86 tons (Thames measurement), 49' long, 14' beam, owned by R. Norris Wolfenden and used for a series of oceanographic cruises between 1899 and 1902.

From June 1899 to June 1900 the *Walwin* made a series of cruises around the Shetlands, occupying a number of relatively shallow stations (less than 100 fathoms) at approximately monthly intervals. Townet and dredge samples were obtained and temperature measurements made at various depths using Miller-Casella maximum-minimum thermometers and Negretti and Zambra reversing thermometers. Some water samples were also obtained with Mill's slip water bottle.

From July 1900 to July 1902 the *Walwin* made a further series of cruises in the Faröe-Shetland Channel, carrying out similar observations to depths of about 500 fathoms (900m). The *Walwin* was too small to accommodate a steam winch and therefore all the work had to be accomplished by hand. From the summer of 1902, Wolfenden replaced the *Walwin* with the larger *Silver Belle* for a series of more extensive cruises and working rather deeper stations with the help of a steam winch.

In August 1900 the *Walwin* was joined by Thomas V. Hodgson to gain some sea-going oceanographic experience in preparation for Scott's expedition on the *Discovery* for which Hodgson had been appointed the biologist.

Preliminary reports on the results of the cruises of the *Walwin* and *Silver Belle* cruises were published by Wolfenden (1909) in the first and only Memoir of the *Challenger* Society.

Reference:
Wolfenden, 1909.

WILLIAM SCORESBY

British steam vessel built by Cook, Welton and Gemmell Ltd., at Beverley, Yorkshire and launched on December 31, 1925. Length overall 134', beam 26', 370 tons displacement, triple expansion 1050 h.p. engines.

The *William Scoresby* was built for the Discovery Committee to join R.R.S. *Discovery* in the investigations of the Southern Ocean. In addition to general oceanographic work, the vessel

R.R.S. William Scoresby *leaving Grytviken, South Georgia. Institute of Oceanographic Sciences Neg. no. 7200.*

was intended to carry out commercial scale trawling and whale marking experiments. She was therefore built on the lines of a whale-catcher, with a speed of some 12 knots and with a very large bunker capacity.

The vessel sailed south in 1926, joining the *Discovery* at Simonstown on 1 August 1926. Between that time and 1938 the *William Scoresby* carried out seven separate commissions, originally with the title R.S.S. (Research Steamship) but with the title R.R.S. (Royal Research Ship) from 1929 when the same title was bestowed on the new *Discovery II*.

For her first commission, in collaboration with the *Discovery* in 1926 and 1927, the *William Scoresby* was under the command of G.M. Mercer and occupied a total of 136 stations in a whale marking and general oceanographic cruise around South Georgia and a trawling survey around the Falkland Islands. For the first leg, from Simonstown to South Georgia, the chief scientist was J.E. Hamilton, a Falklands Government naturalist who had previously been on the *Discovery*. Hamilton was assisted by two zoologists, N.A. Mackintosh and L. Harrison Matthews, and a hydrologist, A.J. Clowes, all of whom had been working at the *Discovery* Expedition's shore station on South Georgia since late 1924, and by F.C. Fraser who had sailed with the vessel from England and later transferred to the *Discovery*. A.C. Hardy, who had been with Kemp on the *Discovery* since she left England in 1925, took over as chief scientist on the *William Scoresby* for the survey around South Georgia in December 1926 and January 1927 and also for the leg from the Falklands via South Georgia to the Cape in May/June 1927.

During the second commission, from 1927 to 1930, the *Scoresby* was under the command first of H. de G. Lamotte and later of R.L.V. Shannon. The chief scientist was initially D. Dilwyn John and later J.W.S. Marr who had first visited the Antarctic with Shackleton on the *Quest*. During the first part of this commission the ship was engaged in general oceanography between the Falklands, South Georgia and the South Shetlands. In 1929 and 1930 she was used as a base ship for Hubert Wilkins' second season of aerial reconnaissance of Antarctica, the previous season's work having used as a base the Hektor Whaling Company vessel *Hektoria*.

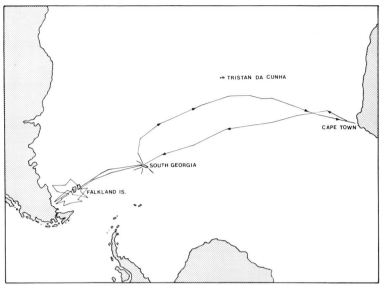

Track of the R.R.S. William Scoresby *during her first commission in 1926 and 1927. Redrawn from* Discovery Reports, *Volume 1.*

From 1930 to 1938 the *William Scoresby* was employed in a series of cruises concerned mainly with whale marking, while the more general oceanographic observations were carried out from the specially built *Discovery II* which replaced the earlier *Discovery* from 1929.

The *Scoresby's* first major whale marking cruise, the vessel's third commission from 1930 to 1932, was spent mainly around South Georgia and in the northern Weddell Sea, but she also carried out a survey of the Peru coastal current and a trawling survey of Burdwood Bank. For this commission E.R. Gunther was the chief scientist, while the vessel was under the command of J.C.C. Irving or T.A Joliffe on different cruises.

On the fourth and fifth commissions, in 1934 / 35 and 1935 / 36 respectively, attention was concentrated on the pelagic whaling grounds south of South Africa and in the southern Indian Ocean under the command of C.R.U. Boothby and with G.W. Rayner as chief scientist.

Boothby was again in command during the sixth commission, in 1936-1937, but with T.J. Hart as chief scientist. This commission concentrated on whale marking in the Indian Ocean sector.

On the seventh and final commission before the war, in 1937 and 1938, Rayner was again chief scientist with R.C. Freaker in command for whale marking in the Scotia and Bellingshausen Seas.

During the whale marking cruises on the *William Scoresby,* and three additional cruises in commercial catchers, more than 5000 whales were tagged of which, by the time Rayner published the results in 1940, 187 had been returned.

From 1939 the *William Scoresby* was taken over by the Admiralty and employed as a minesweeper in the South Atlantic while based in the Falklands, until she was transferred to Operation Tabarin in 1944. This naval operation, named after a Parisian nightclub, had begun in 1943 with the intention of establishing two antarctic bases and to retain allied control of the southern side of Drake Passage. Polar advice was provided by James Wordie, a veteran of the *Endurance* expedition of 1914, Brian Roberts of the British Graham Land Expedition, and Neil Mackintosh, Director of the Discovery Investigations. The vessel originally employed was the Norwegian auxiliary steam sailing ship *Godthaab,* chartered by the Admiralty and renamed H.M.S. *Bransfield* under the command of James Marr, then serving in the RNVR. However, shortly after leaving Tilbury in November 1943, loaded with stores and men for the southern bases, the *Bransfield* sprang a serious leak and had to put into Portsmouth. Her cargo was carried out to the Falklands on other vessels and her role was taken over by the *William Scoresby,* backed up by the Falkland Islands Company vessel the S.S. *Fitzroy.*

By the end of the war three bases had been established, one on Deception Island and two on the Antarctic Peninsula at Port Lockroy and Hope Bay, and meteorological, geological, biological and tidal observations had begun. In 1947 Operation Tabarin was renamed the Falkland Islands Dependencies Survey and its funding was transferred to the Colonial Office. The *William Scoresby* continued to service the bases for the Survey but was purchased by the Admiralty from the Government of the Falkland Islands Dependencies, along with the *Discovery* II, and presented to the newly established National Institute of Oceanography in 1949.

When the vessels were requisitioned for war service their scientific equipment was stored at St Katharine's Dock in London but was destroyed in an air raid in 1940. Accordingly, they had to be refitted and re-equipped for the N.I.O.

Since the Discovery Investigations had been taken over by the new Institute it had been agreed that the two ships initially would continue with the Discovery Committee's programme. Accordingly, the *William Scoresby* sailed from London in January 1950 for her first and only commission for the National Institute, under the command of A.F. Macfie and the scientific direction initially of T.J. Hart, and later of R.H. Clarke, assisted by R.I. Currie. The main effort was spent in whale marking in the South Indian Ocean during the southern winter migration and in an extensive survey of the Benguela Current. Also, a period of ten days was spent in fishing experiments off East London, including the use of a large fish trap, in an unsuccessful effort to obtain a Coelacanth.

When the vessel returned to the U.K. in December 1950 the financial situation was such that she was laid up in Plymouth, with the hope that she could be recommissioned at a later date. In the event this was not possible and she was eventually sold for scrap for £1,900 in 1953.

References:
Bernacchi, 1938; Coleman-Cooke, 1963; Fuchs, 1982; Hardy, 1967; Kemp, Hardy and Mackintosh, 1929; National Institute of Oceanography, 1951; National Oceanographic Council, 1952, 1955

XANTHUS

Steam launch, 22′ long, purchased at Colombo 1905 as a tender to the *Sealark* during the Percy Sladen Trust Expedition. The *Xanthus* was used extensively for surveying and for dredging and townetting in the shallow waters in and around the various atolls visited.

Reference:
Gardiner and Forster Cooper, 1907.

CHRONOLOGICAL LIST

1801-1803	*Investigator*	1865-1868	*Gannet*
1803-1812	*Resolution*	1866-1867	*Salamander*
1816	*Congo* and *Dorothea*	1867	*Hydra*
1816	*Eurydice*	1868	*Lightning*
1816-1817	*Alceste*	1868-1870	*Newport*
1818	*Isabella, Alexander,*	1869-1870	*Porcupine*
	Dorothea and *Trent*	1870	*Norna*
1819-1820	*Hecla* and *Griper*	1870-1872	*Lalla Rookh*
1820-1824	*Baffin*	1870-1873	*Nassau*
1821-1824	*Adventure*	1871	*Shearwater*
1821-1823	*Fury, Hecla*	1872-1876	*Challenger*
1822-1823	*Pheasant*	1874	*Clyde*
1824-1825	*Hecla, Fury*	1875-1876	*Alert, Discovery* and *Valorous*
1825-1828	*Blossom*	1875-1876	*Pandora*
1827	*Hecla*	1878-1882	*Mallard*
1828-1831	*Chanticleer*	1880	*Knight Errant*
1831	*Pike*	1882	*Triton*
1831-1836	*Beagle*	1882-1884	*Lark*
1831-1840	*Fairy*	c1884-1892	*Medusa*
1832	*Trinculo*	1883	*Dacia*
1833-1834	*Aid*	1883-1886	*Flying Fish*
1834	*Medea*	1884-1907	*Investigator*
1835-1842	*Sulphur*	1885-1886	*Buccaneer*
1836	*Thalia*	1885-1888	*Lord Bandon*
1839-1843	*Erebus* and *Terror*	1886-1892	*Garland*
1840-1848	*Shearwater*	1887	*Jackal*
1841-1842	*Beacon* and *Isabella*	1889	*Research*
1842-1845	*Fly, Bramble* and *Castlereagh*	1890	*Fingal*
1843-1846	*Samarang*	1890-1896	*Penguin*
1845-1846	*Pagoda*	1891	*Harlequin*
1845-1848	*Erebus* and *Terror*	1892-1893	*Balaena, Active, Polar Star*
1845-1860	*Herald* and *Pandora*		and *Diana*
1846-1850	*Rattlesnake, Bramble*	1893	*Egeria*
	and *Castlereagh*	1896	*Granuaile*
1846-1848	*Research* (tender to *Beacon*)	1896-1900	*Research*
1848-1849	*Enterprise*	1897	*Egeria*
1851-1856	*Spitfire*	1898	*Oceana*
1854	*Frolic*	1898	*Stork*
1856-1863	*Medina*	1898-1900	*Southern Cross*
1857	*Cyclops*	1899	*Britannia*
1857	*Tartarus*	1899-1902	*Walwin*
1858	*Gorgon*	1901-1904	*Discovery*
1859	*Firebrand*	1901-1908	*Helga*
1860	*Bulldog*	1902-1904	*Scotia*

1902-1905	*Huxley*	1921-1922	*Quest*
1902-1922	*Goldseeker*	1922	*H 32* and *Rocket*
1903-1904	*Terra Nova*	1924-1927	*Discovery*
1903-1905	*Goldfinch*	1926-1950	*William Scoresby*
1903-1907	*Silver Belle*	1927	*Ormonde*
1905	*Sealark* and *Xanthus*	1929-1931	*Discovery*
1907-1909	*Nimrod*	1929-1951	*Discovery II*
1908-1914	*Helga II*	1933-1934	*Mabahiss*
1908-1926	*Investigator*	1937-1938	*Rosaura*
1910-1913	*Terra Nova*	1939	*Research* (not completed)
1911-1913	*Aurora*	1947-c1972	*Manihine*
1914-1917	*Endurance*	1950-1952	*Challenger*
1921	*L 6*		

REFERENCES

ABEL, C. 1818. *Narrative of a journey in the interior of China, and a voyage to and from that country, in the years 1816 and 1817.* London: Longmans, XVI + 420pp.

AGASSIZ, L. 1869. Report upon deep-sea dredgings in the Gulf Stream during the third cruise of the U.S.S. "Bibb". *Bulletin of the Museum of Comparative Zoology, Harvard,* **1**: 363-386.

ALCOCK, A.W. 1898. A summary of the deep-sea zoological work of the Royal Indian Marine Survey Ship *Investigator* from 1884 to 1897. *Scientific Memoirs by Medical Officers of the Army of India,* **XI**: 45-93.

ALCOCK, A.W. 1901. Zoological gleanings from the Royal Indian Marine Survey Ship *Investigator. Scientific Memoirs by Medical Officers of the Army of India,* **XII**: 35-76.

ALLEN, E.J. 1904-06. First report of the Council of the Marine Biological Association of the United Kingdom on work carried out in connection with the International Fishery Investigations. *Journal of the Marine Biological Association of the United Kingdom,* **7**: 383-390.

ANON 1935. The Admiralty magnetic survey ship. *Nature, London,* **135** (3423): 949.

ARDLEY, R.A.B. and MACKINTOSH, N.A. 1936. The Royal Research Ship *Discovery II. Discovery Reports,* **13**: 77-106.

ARNOTT, D. *et al.* 1951. *Report on tonnage measurements.* New York: Society of Naval Architects and Marine Engineers, 18pp.

BACK, G. 1838. *Narrative of an expedition in H.M.S. Terror, undertaken with a view to geographical discovery on the Arctic shores, in the years 1836-7, by Captain Back.* London: John Murray, VII + 456pp.

BAGLEHOLE, K.C. 1969. *A Century of Service: a brief history of Cable and Wireless Ltd., 1868-1968.* London: Cable and Wireless Ltd. 54pp.

BARNABY, K.C. 1960. *Basic naval architecture.* London: Hutchinson, 482pp.

BARTSCH, P., REHDER, H.A. and SHIELDS, B.E. 1946. A bibliography and short biographical sketch of William Healey Dall. *Smithsonian Miscellaneous Collections,* **104**: 15: 1-96.

BASSETT-SMITH, P.W. 1893. *Report on the results of dredgings obtained on the Macclesfield Bank, by HMS "Penguin", Commander W.U. Moore, R.N., April 1892.* London: H.M.S.O., 16pp.

BASSETT-SMITH, P.W. 1894. *Report on the results of dredgings obtained on the Macclesfield Bank, in H.M.S. "Rambler", H.M.S. "Penguin" and H.M.S. "Egeria".* London: H.M.S.O., 42pp.

BASSETT-SMITH, P.W. 1895. Survey of the Macclesfield Bank, South China Seas. *Geographical Journal,* **5**: 73-75.

BEECHEY, F.W. 1831 *Narrative of a voyage to the Pacific and Bering's Strait, to co-operate with the Polar Expeditions: performed in H.M.S Blossom, in the years 1825-1828,* London: 2 vols, 472 + 452pp.

BEECHEY, F.W. 1843. *Voyage of discovery towards the North Pole.* London: 351pp.

BELCHER, E. 1848. *Narrative of the voyage of H.M.S. Samarang during the years 1843-46.* London: Reeve, Bencham and Reeve, 2 vols, 358 + 573pp.

BENCKER, H. 1944. Chronological list of the main maritime discoveries and explorations. *Hydrographic Review,* **21**: 130-174.

BERNACCHI, L. 1901. *To the South Polar Regions. Expedition of 1898-1900.* London: Hurst and Blackett, XVI + 348pp.

BERNACCHI, L.C. 1938. *The Saga of the Discovery.* London and Glasgow: Blackie and Son.

BERNSTEIN, R.E. 1985. The Scottish National Antarctic Expedition 1902-04. *Polar Record,* **22**: 379-392.

BOCKSTOCE, J.R. 1985. The search for Sir John Franklin in Alaska. Pp. 93-113 in Sutherland, P.D. [Ed.] *The Franklin era in Canadian Arctic history 1845-1859.* National Museum of Man, Mercury Series, Archaeological Survey of Canada, Paper no. 131.

BOOG WATSON, W.N. 1969. The Scottish Marine Station for Scientific Research, Granton, 1884-1903. *The Book of the Old Edinburgh Club,* **33**: 50-58.

BORCHGREVINK, C.E. 1900. The "Southern Cross" Expedition to the Antarctic 1899-1900. *Geographical Journal*, **16** (4): 381-414.

BORCHGREVINK, C.E. 1901. *First on the Antarctic Continent, being an account of the British Antarctic Expedition, 1898-1900.* London: George Newnes Ltd., 333pp. (Republished in 1980 by C. Hurst and Company, London).

BOURNE, G.C. 1889-90. Report on a trawling cruise in H.M.S. *Research* off the south-west coast of Ireland. *Journal of the Marine Biological Association of the United Kingdom*, New Series, **1**: 306-323.

BRENT, P. 1981. *Charles Darwin.* London: William Heinemann, 536pp.

BRITISH ANTARCTIC EXPEDITION, 1907-1909. *Report on the Scientific Investigations.* London: W. Heinemann, 4 volumes (published 1910-1916).

BROWN, R.N.R. 1923. *A naturalist at the poles. The life, work and voyages of Dr. W.S. Bruce, the polar explorer.* London: Seeley, Service and Co. 316pp.

BROWN, R.N.R., MOSSMAN, R.C. and PIRIE, J.H.H. 1906. *Voyage of the Scotia.* Edinburgh: Blackwood, 375pp.

BRUCE, W.S. 1896. Cruise of the "Balaena" and the "Active" in the Antarctic seas, 1892-93. I. The "Balaena". *Geographical Journal,* **7** (5): 502-521.

BUCHANAN, J.Y. 1884-6. On oceanic shoals discovered in the S.S. *Dacia* in October 1883. *Proceedings of the Royal Society of Edinburgh*, **13**: 428-443.

BUCHANAN, J.Y. 1887. On the land slopes separating continents and ocean basins, especially those on the west coast of Africa. *Scottish Geographical Magazine*, **3**: 217-238.

BUCHANAN, J.Y. 1888. The exploration of the Gulf of Guinea. *Scottish Geographical Magazine*, **4**: 177-200, 233-251.

BUCHANAN, J.Y. 1919. *Accounts rendered of work done and things seen.* Cambridge University Press. vii + 435pp.

BUCHANAN, R.A. and DOUGHTY, M.W. 1978. The choice of steam engine manufacturers by the British Admiralty, 1822-1852. *Mariner's Mirror*, **64** (4): 327-346.

BUEN, R. de 1927. Resultats des investigations espagnoles dans le Detroit de Gibraltar. *Rapport et Proces-verbaux des Reunions du Conseil Permanent International pour l'Exploration de la Mer*, **44**: 60-91.

BURSTYN, H.L. 1968. Science and government in the nineteenth century: the *Challenger* Expedition and its Report. *Bulletin de l'Institut Oceanographique, Monaco*, special number 2: 603-613.

BURSTYN, H.L. 1972. Pioneering in large-scale scientific organisation: the *Challenger* Expedition and its Report. I. Launching the expedition. *Proceedings of the Royal Society of Edinburgh*, B **72**: 47-61.

BURSTYN, H.L. 1975. Science pays off: Sir John Murray and the Christmas Island phosphate industry 1886-1914. *Social Studies of Science*, **5**: 5-34.

CAMPBELL, Lord G. 1877. *Log-letters from "The Challenger"*, London: Macmillan, 504pp.

CARPENTER, W.B. 1868-69. Preliminary report of dredging operations in the seas to the north of the British Isles, carried on in H.M.S. *Lightning*, by Dr. Carpenter and Dr. Wyville Thomson, Professor of Natural History in Queen's College, Belfast. *Proceedings of the Royal Society of London*, **17**: 169-200; 198-199.

CARPENTER, W.B. 1872. Report on the scientific researches carried on during the months of August, September and October, 1871, in H.M. Surveying Ship *Shearwater*. *Proceedings of the Royal Society of London*, **20**: 535-644.

CARPENTER, W.B. 1876. Report on the physical investigations carried on by P. Herbert Carpenter in HMS Valorous during her return voyage from Disco Island in August 1875. *Proceedings of the Royal Society of London*, **25** (173): 230-237.

CARPENTER, W.B., and JEFFREYS, J.G. 1870-71. Report on deep-sea researches carried on during the months of July, August and September 1870, in H.M.S. *Porcupine*. *Proceedings of the Royal Society of London*, **19**: 146-221.

CARPENTER, W.B., JEFFREYS, J.G. and THOMSON, C.W. 1869-70. Preliminary report on the scientific exploration of the deep sea in H.M.S. *Porcupine*, during the summer of 1869. *Proceedings of the Royal Society of London*, **18**: 397-492.

CHARNOCK, H. 1973. *Challenger* and the development of marine science. *Journal of Navigation*, **26** (1): 1-12.

CHIMMO, W. 1869. Soundings and temperatures in the Gulf Stream. *Proceedings of the Royal Geographical Society*, **13**: 92-101.

CHIMMO, W. 1870. *Bed of the Atlantic.* 41pp inc. reprint of Chimmo, 1869, apparently published privately by Chimmo.

CHUMLEY, J. 1918. *The Fauna of the Clyde Sea area: being an attempt to record the zoological results obtained by the late Sir J. Murray and his assistants on board the S.Y. "Medusa" during. . . 1884-1892.* Glasgow: University Press, VI + 200pp.

COLEMAN-COOKE, J. 1963. *Discovery II in the Antarctic.* London: Odhams, 255pp.

COLLINS, T. 1985. *Floreat Hibernia: a bio-bibliography of Robert Lloyd Praeger 1865-1953.* Royal Dublin Society, XIV + 151pp.

COLLINSON, R. 1889. *Journal of H.M.S. "Enterprise" on the expedition in search of Sir John Franklin's ships by Behring Strait, 1850-55.* London: Low, Marston, Searle and Rivington.

COLMAN, J.S. 1954. The "Rosaura" Expedition. *Bulletin of the British Museum (Natural History),* Zoology, **2**: 115-239.

COPPINGER, R.W. 1883. *Cruise of the "Alert". Four years in Patagonian, Polynesian, and Mascarene waters (1878-82).* London: W. Swan Sonnenschein and Co., XV + 256pp.

COPPINGER, R.W. 1884. Summary of the Voyage, Pp. 1-4 in *Report on the zoological collections made in the Indo-Pacific Ocean during the voyage of HMS 'Alert', 1881-1882.* London: British Museum (Natural History), XXV: 684pp.

COOK, F.A. 1900. *Through the first Antarctic night.* London: Heinemann, 478pp.

COOKE, A. and HOLLAND, C. 1978. *The exploration of Northern Canada, 500 to 1920. A chronology.* The Arctic History Press, 549pp.

CUNNINGHAM, J.T. 1885. *The Scottish Marine Station for Scientific Research, Granton, Edinburgh. Its work and prospects.* Edinburgh.

CYRIAX, R.J. 1939. *Sir John Franklin's last Arctic expedition.* London: Methuen.

DARLING, L. 1978. H.M.S. *Beagle*: further research or twenty years a-Beagling. *Mariner's Mirror,* **64** (4): 315-325.

DARWIN, C. 1859. *On the origin of species by means of natural selection, or the preservation of favoured races in the struggle for life.* London: John Murray, 502pp.

DAVIS, J.K. 1919. *With the "Aurora" in the Antarctic, 1911-1914.* London: Andrew Melrose, 183pp.

DAWSON, L.S. 1885. *Memoirs of Hydrography, including brief biographies of the principal officers who have served in H.M. Naval Surveying Service between the years 1750 and 1885.* Eastbourne: Henry W. Keay, 2 vols. 133 and 209pp. [Reprinted 1969 by Cornmarket Press, London].

DAY, A. 1967. *The Admiralty hydrographic service—1795-1919.* London: H.M.S.O. 378pp.

DAYMAN, J. 1858. *Deep sea soundings in the North Atlantic Ocean between Ireland and Newfoundland, made in H.M.S. Cyclops in June and July 1857.* London: H.M.S.O. 73pp.

DAYMAN, J. 1859. *Deep sea soundings in the North Atlantic Ocean between Newfoundland, the Azores and England, made in H.M.S. Gorgon, in September and October 1858.* London: H.M.S.O. 30pp.

DAYMAN, J. 1860. *Deep sea soundings in the Bay of Biscay and Mediterranean Sea, made in H.M.S. Firebrand, in the summer of 1859.* London: H.M.S.O. 43pp.

DEACON, G.E.R. 1975. The oceanographical observations of Scott's last expedition. *Polar Record,* **17** (109): 391-396.

DEACON, G.E.R. and RICE, A.L. 1984. The significance of the John Murray/*Mabahiss* Expedition to the Arabian Sea. *Deep-Sea Research,* **31**: 573-581.

DEACON, M.B. 1971. *Scientists and the sea 1650-1900: a study of marine science,* London: Academic Press, xvi + 445pp.

DEACON, M.B. 1977. Staff Commander Tizard's journal and the voyages of H.M. Ships *Knight Errant* and *Triton* to the Wyville Thomson Ridge in 1880 and 1882. Pp. 1-14 in Angel, M.V. [Ed.] *A Voyage of Discovery,* Oxford: Pergamon Press.

DEACON, M.B. 1978. Vice-Admiral T.A.B. Spratt and the development of oceanography in the Mediterranean 1841-1873. *Maritime Monographs and Reports,* No. 37: V + 74pp.

DEACON, M.B. 1984. G. Herbert Fowler (1861-1940): the forgotten oceanographer. *Notes and Records of the Royal Society of London,* **38**: 261-296.

DEACON, M.B. 1985. An early theory of ocean circulation: J.S. von Waitz and his explanation of the currents in the Strait of Gibraltar. *Progress in Oceanography*, **14**: 89-101.

DEACON, M.B. and DEACON, G.E.R. 1972. The first oceanographic expedition. Geographical Magazine, **44**, (12), 863-866.

DEACON, M.B. and SAVOURS, A. 1976. Sir George Strong Nares (1831-1915). *Polar Record*, **18**: (113): 127-141.

DE COURCY IRELAND, J. 1981. *Ireland's sea fisheries: a history.* Dublin: The Glendale Press, 184pp.

DEPARTMENT OF AGRICULTURE AND TECHNICAL INSTRUCTION FOR IRELAND, 1902. *Ireland Industrial and Agricultural.* Brown and Nolan, 532pp.

DICKSON, H.N. 1893. Report on physical investigations carried out on board H.M.S. 'Jackal', 1893-94. *Twelfth Annual Report. Fisheries Board, Scotland*, 1893.

DIETZ, R.S. and KNEBEL, H.J. 1968. Survey of Ross's deep sea sounding site. *Nature, London*, **220** (5169): 751-753.

DODGE, E.S. 1973. *The Polar Rosses. John and James Clark Ross and their explorations.* London: Faber and Faber, 260pp.

DONALD, C.W. 1896. Cruise of the "Balaena" and the "Active" in the Antarctic seas, 1892-93. II. The "Active". *Geographical Journal*, **7** (5): 625-643.

DOUGLAS, H.P. 1929. Current measurements in the Strait of Gibraltar made in H.M.S. *Goldfinch* in 1905. *Rapport et Proces-verbaux des Reunions du Conseil Permanent International pour l'Exploration de la Mer*, **67**: 7-14.

EAST AFRICAN MARINE FISHERIES RESEARCH ORGANIZATION 1958. *Annual Report*, 1956-1957, 24pp.

EDGELL, J.A. 1938. R.R.S. *Research. Hydrographic Review*, **85** (2): 7-8.

EVANS, H.B. 1974. The *Southern Cross* Expedition, 1898-1900: a personal account. *Polar Record*, **17** (106): 23-29.

EVANS, H.B. and JONES, A.G.E. 1974. A forgotten explorer. Carsten Egeberg Borchgrevink. *Polar Record*, **17** (108): 221-235.

FARRAN, G.P. 1928. L'etat libre d'Irlande. pp. 183-185 in *Rapport Jubilaire 1902-1927. Rapport et Proces-Verbaux des Reunions du Conseil Permanent International pour l'Exploration de la Mer*, **47**: 152-185.

FISHER, M. and FISHER, J. 1957. *Shackleton.* London: Barrie Books Ltd., 559pp.

FITZROY, R. 1836. Sketch of the surveying voyages of H.M.S. *Adventure* and *Beagle*, 1825-36. *Geographical Journal*, **6**: 311-343.

FITZROY, R. 1839. *Narrative of the surveying voyages of H.M.S. Adventure and Beagle, between the years 1826 and 1836, describing their examination of the southern shores of South America, and the Beagle's circumnavigation of the globe.* London: 3 vols., 597 + 694 + 629pp.

FLETCHER, H. 1984. *Antarctic days with Mawson. A personal account of the British Australian and New Zealand Antarctic Research Expedition of 1929-31.* London: Angus and Robertson.

FLINDERS, M. 1814. *A voyage to Terra Australis . . . in . . . 1801-1803 in H.M.S. the Investigator.* London: 2 vols.

FORBES, E. 1844(a). Report on the Mollusca and Radiata of the Aegean Sea, and on their distribution, considered as bearing on geology. *Report of the British Association for the Advancement of Science*, York 1843: 130-193.

FORBES, E. 1844(b). On the light thrown on geology by submarine researches; being the substance of a communication made to the Royal Institution of Great Britain, Friday evening, the 23rd February, 1844. *Edinburgh New Philosophical Journal*, **36**: 318-327.

FORBES, E. and GODWIN-AUSTIN, R. 1859. *The Natural History of the European Sea.* London: John Van Voorst, 360pp.

FOSTER, M. and LANKESTER, E. Ray [Eds] 1900. *The Scientific memoirs of Thomas Henry Huxley.* London.

FOWLER, G.H. 1896. Contributions to our knowledge of the plankton of the Faeroe Channel–No. 1. *Proceedings of the General Meetings for Scientific Business of Zoological Society of London for year 1896*: 991-996.

FOWLER, G.H. 1898. Contributions to our knowledge of the plankton of the Faeroe Channel. VI. Description of a new mid-water tow-net. Discussion of the mid-water fauna (mesoplankton) etc. *Proceedings of the Zoological Society of London*, (1898): 567-585.

FUCHS, V. 1982. *Of ice and men.* Anthony Nelson, 383pp.

GARDINER, J.S. and FORSTER COOPER, C. 1907. Description of the Expedition. In: Percy Sladen Trust Expedition to the Indian Ocean in 1905. *Transactions of the Linnean Society of London*, 2nd ser., **12**: 1-56 and 111-175.

GARDINER, R. 1979. [Ed.] *Conway's All the World's fighting ships, 1860-1895.* London: Conway Maritime Press, 440pp.

GASKELL, T.F. 1960. *Under Deep Oceans.* London: Eyre and Spottiswoode, 240pp.

GEDGE, H.J. 1898. *Report on the undercurrents in the Straits of Bab-el-Mandeb.* London: Hydrographic Department.

GIRDLER, R.W. 1984. The evolution of the Gulf of Aden and Red Sea in space and time. *Deep-Sea Research*, **31**: 747-762.

GOSSET, W.P. 1986. *The lost ships of the Royal Navy, 1793-1900.* London and New York: Mansell Publishing Company, 157pp.

GOULD, R.T. 1924. The Ross Deep. *Geographical Journal*, **63**: 237-241.

GREEN, C. 1908-09. The Department's fishery cruiser, "Helga". *Journal of the Department of Agriculture and Technical Instruction for Ireland*, **9**: 23-28.

GREEN, W.S. 1889. Report of a deep-sea trawling cruise off the S.W. coast of Ireland, under the direction of Rev. W. Spotswood Green. Summary of the cruise. *Annals and Magazine of Natural History*, Ser. VI, **4**: 409-414.

GREEN, W.S. 1890-1891 Report of the Fisheries Committee. *Proceedings of the Royal Dublin Society*, Appendix E, **127**: 26-66.

GREEN, W.S. 1891-1892. Survey of the fishing grounds on West Coast—report to the Fisheries Committee. *Proceedings of the Royal Dublin Society*, Appendix C, **128**: 23-239.

GRIERSON, J. 1964. *Challenge to the poles. Highlights of arctic and antarctic aviation.* London: G.T. Foulis and Co., 695pp.

GUPPY, H.B. 1882-1885. Observations on the recent calcareous formations of the Solomon Group made during 1882-84. *Transactions of the Royal Society of Edinburgh*, (1882-1885): **32**: 545-581.

GUPPY, H.B. 1884-1886. Notes on the characters and modes of formations of the coral reefs of the Solomon Islands, being the results of observations made in 1882-84 during the surveying cruise of H.M.S. *Lark. Proceedings of the Royal Society of Edinburgh*, (1884-1886): **13**: 857-904.

HADDON, A.C. and GREEN, W.S. 1887. Second report on the marine fauna of the south-west of Ireland. *Proceedings of the Royal Irish Academy*, **1** (Series 3): 29-56.

HAIGH, K.R. 1968. *Cableships and submarine cables.* London: Adlard Coles Ltd. 416pp.

HARDY, A.C. 1967. *Great Waters.* London: Collins, 542pp.

HATTERSLEY-SMITH, G. 1976. The British Arctic Expedition, 1875-76. *Polar Record*, **18** (113): 117-126.

HEDGEPETH, J.W. 1946. The voyage of the *Challenger. Scientific Monthly*, **63**: 194-202.

HINDS, R.B. 1844. *Zoology of the voyage of H.M.S. Sulphur under the command of Capt. Edward Belcher, R.N. during the years 1836-42.* London: 2 vols., 150 + 72pp.

HISARD, P. 1983. Deux precurseurs de l'etude du Golfe de Guinee an XIXeme siecle: Charles-Philippe de Kerhallet et John Young Buchanan. *Oceanographie tropicale*, **18**: 95-101.

HISARD, P. 1986. Centenaire de la decouverte du sous-courant equatorial dans l'ocean Atlantique par J.Y. Buchanan, 9-11 mars 1886. *Oceanologica Acta*, **9**:

HOGG, R.S. 1956. *Naval architecture and ship construction.* London: Institute of Marine Engineers.

HOLT, E.W.L. 1892, Survey of fishing grounds, west coast of Ireland, 1890-1891. Report on the results of the fishing operations. *Scientific Proceedings of the Royal Dublin Society*, **7** (4): 225-483.

HOOKER, J.D. 1847. *Flora Antarctica. The botany of the Antarctic voyage of H.M. Discovery ships Erebus and Terror, in the years 1839-1843. Under the command of Captain Sir James Clark Ross, Kt., R.N., F.R.S.*. London: Reeve Bros., 687pp.

HOSKYN, R. 1862. *Report of deep sea soundings west of Ireland made in HMS Porcupine in June, July and August 1862*. London: Hydrographic Department. [Publication H.D. 19].

HUNTFORD, R. 1985. *Shackleton*. London: Hodder and Stoughton, 774pp.

HUXLEY, L. 1900. *Life and letters of Thomas Henry Huxley*. London: Macmillan, 2 vols.

HUXLEY, L. (Ed.) 1913. *Scott's Last Expedition*, London: Smith, Elder and Co., 2 vols., 633 + 534pp.

HUXLEY, L. 1918. *Life and letters of Sir Joseph Dalton Hooker O.M., G.C.S.I. Based on materials collected by Lady Hooker*. London: John Murray, Vol. 1, 546pp.

HUXLEY, T.H. 1868. On some organisms which live at the bottom of the north Atlantic, in depths of 6000 to 15000 feet. *Report. British Association for the Advancement of Science*, 1868: 102.

HUXLEY, T.H. 1875. Notes from the *Challenger. Nature, London*, **12**: 315-316.

HUXLEY, T.H. 1936. *T.H. Huxley's diary of the voyage of H.M.S. Rattlesnake*. Ed. J. Huxley. New York: Doubleday. 301pp.

INTERNATIONAL COUNCIL FOR THE EXPLORATION OF THE SEA, 1928. Rapport Jubilaire (1902-1927). *Rapport et Proces-Verbaux des Reunions du Conseil Permanent International pour l'Exploration de la Mer*, **27**: 271pp.

JEFFREYS, J.G. et al. 1876. Preliminary report of the biological results of a cruise in H.M.S. *Valorous* to Davis Strait in 1875, *Proceedings of the Royal Society of London*, **25** (173): 177-230.

JOHNSON, R.E. 1976. *Sir John Richardson, arctic explorer, natural historian naval surgeon*. London: Taylor and Francis, xii + 209pp.

JONES, A.G.E. 1970. Lieutenant T.E.L. Moore, R.N. and the voyage of the *Pagoda* 1845. *Mariner's Mirror*, **56**: 33-40.

JONES, A.G.E. 1971. Sir James Clark Ross and the voyage of the *Enterprise* and *Investigator*, 1848-49. *Geographical Journal*, **137**: 165-179.

JONES, A.G.E. 1972a. Sir John Ross and Sir John Barrow. *Notes and Queries, London*, N.S. **19**: 294-303.

JONES, A.G.E. 1972b. The voyage of the *Terra Nova. Geographical Journal*, **138**: 309-315.

JONES, A.G.E. 1973. Harry MacKay, master of the *Terra Nova. Antarctic*, **6** (9): 6pp.

JONES, A.G.E. 1974. Dr. W.H.B. Webster 1793-1875, Antarctic scientist. *Polar Record*, **17** (107): 143-145.

JONES, A.G.E. 1975. Obituary of Hugh Blackwall Evans. *Polar Record*, **17** (110): 573-574.

JONES, A.G.E. 1976. Commander D.C. Clavering's voyage to East Greenland, 1823. *Musk-Ox*, **19**: 15-20.

JUKES, J.B. 1847. *Narrative of the surveying voyage of H.M.S. Fly, commanded by Captain F.P. Blackwood, R.N. in Torres Strait, New Guinea, and other islands of the Eastern Archipelago, during the years 1842-1846*. London: T.& W. Boone, 2 vols., 423 and 362pp.

KEMP, P. [Ed.] 1976. *The Oxford companion to ships and the sea*. Oxford University Press.

KEMP, S., HARDY, A.C. and MACKINTOSH, N.A. 1929. Objects, equipment and methods. *Discovery Reports*, **1**: 141-232.

KENT, W.S. 1870. On the Hexactinellidae, or hexradiate spiculed siliceous sponges taken on the "Norna" Expedition off the coast of Spain and Portugal. With description of new species, and revision of the order. *Monthly Microscopical Journal*, **4**: 241-252.

KENT, W.S. 1871. Zoological results of the 1870 dredging expedition of the yacht "Norna" off the coast of Spain and Portugal. *Nature, London*, **4**: 456-458.

KIRWAN, L.P. 1959. *The white road. A survey of polar exploration*. London: Hollis and Carter, 374pp.

KRUMMEL, O. 1910. Ein Blick auf die neueren Theorien der Meereströmungen. *Verhandlungen des 17. Deutschen Geographentages zu Lubeck*, Berlin

KRUMMEL, O. 1911. *Handbuch für Ozeanographie*. Stutgart: 2 vols., 526 + 766pp.

LAING, E.A.M. 1980. The introduction of paddle frigates into the Royal Navy. Mariner's Mirror, **66** (4): 331-343.

LE DANOIS, E. 1948. *Les profondeurs de la mer*. Paris: Payot. 303pp.

LEWIS, M.J.T. 1971. *Erebus* and *Terror. Journal of the Railway and Canal Historical Society*, **17** (4): 65-68.

LINDSAY, D.M. 1911. *A voyage to the Arctic in the whaler Aurora*, London: Kegan Paul, 223pp.

LINKLATER, E. 1972. *The voyage of the Challenger*. London: John Murray, 288pp.

LLOYD, C. 1970. *Mr. Barrow of the Admiralty*, London: Collins. 224pp.

LYELL, C. 1833. *Principles of Geology, being an attempt to explain the former changes of the earth's surface, by reference to causes now in operation*. London: John Murray, 3 vols., 511 + 333 + 398pp.

LYONS, H.G. 1924. *Miscellaneous data. British (Terra Nova) Antarctic Expedition 1910-1913*. London: Harrison and Sons, for the Committee of the Captain Scott Antarctic Fund, 75pp.

MacGAHAN, J.A. 1876. *Under the Northern Lights*. London: Sampson Low, 339pp.

MacGILLIVRAY, J. 1852. *Narrative of the voyage of H.M.S. Rattlesnake commanded by the late Captain Owen Stanley, R.N., F.R.S. etc. during the years 1846-1850*. London: T. and W. Boone, 2 vols.

McCONNELL, A. 1982. *No sea too deep*, Bristol: Adam Hilger, 162pp.

M'CLINTOCK, F.L. 1861. *Remarks illustrative of the sounding voyage of H.M.S. Bulldog in 1860*. London: 12pp.

M'CLURE, R.J. Le M. 1857. *The discovery of the North-West Passage by H.M.S. "Investigator", Captain R. M'Clure, 1850, 1851, 1852, 1853, 1854*. London: Longman, Brown, Green, Longmans and Roberts.

MANSELL, A.L. 1857. Deep soundings between Alexandria, Rhodes and Smyrna. *Nautical Magazine*, **26**: 505-512.

MARCET, A. 1819. On the specific gravity, and temperature of sea waters, in different parts of the ocean, and in particular seas; with some account of their contents. *Philosophical Transactions of the Royal Society of London*, **109**: 161-208.

MARKHAM, A.H. 1888, Hudson's Bay and Hudson's Strait as a navigable channel. *Proceedings of the Royal Geographical Society*, **9**: 549-567.

MARSHALL, N.B. 1950. The work of the motor yacht *Manihine. Nature, London*, **166**: 763-764.

MARSHALL, N.B. 1952. Recent biological investigations in the Red Sea. *Endeavour*, **11**: 137-142.

MATTHAUS, W. 1969. Zur entdeckungsgeschichte des Aquatorialen Unterstroms im Atlantischen Ozean. *Beitrage zur Meereskunde*, **23**: 37-70.

MATTHEWS, D.H., LAUGHTON, A.S., PUGH, D.T., JONES, E.J.W., SUNDERLAND, J., TAKIN, M. and BACON, M. 1969. Crustal structure and origin of the Peake and Freen Deeps, N-E Atlantic. *Geophysical Journal of the Royal Astronomical Society*, **18**: 517-542.

MATTHEWS, D.J. 1926. Physical oceanography. In: Percy Sladen Trust Expedition to the Indian Ocean in 1905, vol. 8. *Transactions of the Linnean Society of London*, 2nd ser., **19**: 169-205.

MATTHEWS, D.J. 1927. Temperature and salinity observations in the Gulf of Aden. *Nature, London*, **120**: p.512.

MATTHEWS, D.J. 1928. Temperature and salinity observations in the Gulf of Aden. *Nature, London*, **121**: p. 92.

MATTHEWS, D.J., TAYLOR, G.I. and CRAWSHAY, L.R. 1914. *Ice observation; meteorology and oceanography in the North Atlantic Ocean. Report on the work carried out by the S.S. Scotia, 1913*. London: H.M.S.O., 141pp.

MAWSON, D. 1915. *The home of the blizzard: being the story of the Australasian Antarctic Expedition, 1911-1914*, London: Heinemann, 2vols., 349 + 338pp.

MERRIMAN, D. 1972. Challengers of Neptune: the 'Philosophers'. *Proceedings of the Royal Society of Edinburgh*, B, **72**: 15-45.

MILL, H. R. 1951. *Hugh Robert Mill: an autobiography*. London, New York and Toronto: Geographical Publishers Ltd., 224pp.

MILLS, E.L. 1972. T.R.R. Stebbing, the *Challenger* and knowledge of deep-sea Amphipoda. *Proceedings of the Royal Society of Edinburgh*, B, **72**: 69-87.

MILLS, E.L. 1973(a). H.M.S. *Challenger*, Halifax and the Reverend Dr. Honeyman. *Dalhousie Review*, **53**: 529-545.

MILLS, E.L. 1973(b). *On hundred years of oceanography: essays commemorating the visit of H.M.S. Challenger to Halifax, May 9-19, 1873*, Dalhousie University, 89pp.

MILLS, E.L. 1978. Edward Forbes, John Gwyn Jeffreys, and British dredging before the *Challenger* expedition. *Journal of the Society for the Bibliography of Natural History*, **8** (4): 507-536.

MILLS, E.L. 1980. Alexander Agassiz, Carl Chun and the problem of the intermediate fauna, Pp. 360-372 in Sears, M. and Merriman, D. [Eds]. *Oceanography: the past*, New York: Springer Verlag, 812pp.

MILLS, E.L. 1984. A view of Edward Forbes, naturalist. *Archives of Natural History*, **11** (3): 365-393.

MILNE, P.H. 1972. Oceanography in Scottish sea lochs and estuaries in the nineteenth century and early twentieth centuries. *Proceedings of the Royal Society of Edinburgh*, B, **72**: 459-462.

MOORE, T.E.L. 1846. Magnetic voyage of the *Pagoda. Nautical Magazine*, **1846**: p. 21.

MOORE, W.U. 1899. *Report on observations of the tidal currents and undercurrents in the Strait of Dover made with a deep-sea current meter*. London: H.M.S.O., 17pp.

MOORE, W.U. 1896. *Reports of proceedings in connection with investigations into the physical conditions of the water of the Faeroe Channel*. London: H.M.S.O., 32pp.

MOORE, W.U. and BASSETT-SMITH, P.W. 1889. *Reports of the results of an examination by the officers of H.M.S. "Rambler" of the slopes and zoological condition of Tizard and Macclesfield Banks, 1888*. London: H.M.S.O., 19pp.

MORRIS, J. 1978. *Farewell the trumpets. An imperial retreat*. Faber and Faber, 576pp.

MOSELEY, H.N. 1879. *Notes by a naturalist. An account of observations made during the voyage of H.M.S. Challenger*. London: Macmillan, 620pp.

MOYNE, Lord 1938. *Atlantic Circle*. London and Glasgow: Blackie and Son Ltd., 201pp.

MURDOCH, W.G.B. 1894. *From Edinburgh to the Antarctic: an artist's notes and sketches during the Dundee Antarctic Expedition of 1892-93*. London: Longman, Green, 364pp.

MURRAY, G. 1899. Exploration of the intermediate depths of the ocean. *Geographical Journal*, **13**: 147-154.

MURRAY, J. 1887. On some recent deep-sea observations in the Indian Ocean. *Scottish Geographical Magazine*, **III**: 553-561.

MURRAY, J. 1895. A summary of the scientific results .... *Report on the Scientific Results of the Voyage of H.M.S. Challenger during ... 1873-76, Summary*, 1608pp. in 2 vols.

MURRAY, J. and HJORT, J. 1912. *The Depths of the Ocean*. London: Macmillan, 821pp.

NANSEN, F. 1898. *Farthest North*. London: George Newnes Ltd., 2 vols., 480 and 456pp.

NARES, G.S. 1878. *Narrative of a voyage to the polar sea during 1875-6 in H.M. ships Alert and Discovery*. London: Sampson Low, Marston, Searle and Rivington, 2 vols., 395 + 378pp.

NATIONAL INSTITUTE OF OCEANOGRAPHY 1951. Annual Report, 1949-50. Cambridge University Press, 48pp.

NATIONAL OCEANOGRAPHIC COUNCIL 1952. Annual Report, 1950-51. Cambridge University Press, 26pp.

NATIONAL OCEANOGRAPHIC COUNCIL 1955. Annual Report, 1953-54. Cambridge University Press, 28pp.

OSBON, G.A. 1981. The introduction of paddle frigates into the Royal Navy. *Mariner's Mirror*, **67** (2): 204.

OSBON, G.A. 1982. Paddlewheel fighting ships of the Royal Navy. *Mariner's Mirror*, **68**: 429-433.

O'RIORDAN, C.E. 1967. Some notes on the "Flying Falcon" expedition of 1888, off the south-west coast of Ireland. *Proceedings of the Royal Irish Academy*, **65B**: 373-384.

PARRY, A. 1963. *Parry of the Arctic*. London: Chatto and Windus, 240pp.

PARRY, W.E. 1821. *Journal of a voyage for the Discovery of a North-West Passage from the Atlantic to the Pacific; performed in the years 1819-20, in His Majesty's Ships Hecla and Griper, under the orders of William Edward Parry, R.N., F.R.S., and Commander of the Expedition*. London: John Murray, 310pp + clxxix.

PARRY, W.E. 1824. *Journal of a second voyage for the Discovery of a North-West Passage from the Atlantic to the Pacific; performed in the years 1821-22-23, in His Majesty's Ships Fury and Hecla, under the orders of Captain William Edward Parry, R.N., F.R.S., and Commander of the Expedition*. London: John Murray, 572pp.

PARRY, W.E. 1826. *Journal of a third voyage for the discovery of a North-West Passage from the Atlantic to the Pacific; performed in the years 1824-25, in His Majesty's Ships Hecla and Fury, under the orders of William Edward Parry, R.N., F.R.S., and Commander of the Expedition.* London: John Murray, 186 + 151pp.

PARRY, W.E. 1828. *Narrative of an attempt to reach the North Pole, in boats fitted for the purpose, and attached to His Majesty's Ship Hecla, in the year 1827, under the Command of Captain William Edward Parry, R.N., F.R.S.* London: John Murray, XII + 229pp.

PEAKE, R.E. 1901. *On the results of a deep-sea sounding expedition in the North Atlantic during the summer of 1899.* London: John Murray, 44pp.

PEARSALL, A.W.H. 1973. Bomb vessels. *Polar Record* 16 (105): 781-788.

PEEL, H. 1894. *Polar gleams. An account of a voyage on the yacht "Blencathra".* London: Edward Arnold, 211pp.

PHIPPS, C. 1774. *A voyage towards the North Pole,* London: 253pp.

PRAEGER, R.L. 1937. *The way that I went.* Dublin: Hodges, Figgis, 416pp.

PRESTON, A. and MAJOR, J. 1967. *Send a gunboat. A study of the gunboat and its role in British policy, 1854-1904.* London: Longmans, Green and Co., 266pp.

PRICE, A. Grenfell 1963. Geographical report. *Reports of the British, Australian and New Zealand Antarctic Research Expedition, 1929-1931,* Ser. A, Vol. 1, 241pp.

PULLAR, L. 1910. *Lengthening shadows: random notes of a family history written in old age.* Published privately.

REHBOCK, P.F. 1975. Huxley, Haeckel, and the oceanographers: the case of *Bathybius haeckelii. Isis,* **66**: 604-533.

REHBOCK, P.F. 1979. The early dredgers: "naturalizing" in British seas, 1830-1850. *Journal of the History of Biology,* **12**: 293-368.

ROBERTS, B. 1958. Chronological list of antarctic expeditions. *Polar Record,* **9**: 97-134 and 191-239.

RICE, A.L. 1972. H.M.S. *Challenger;* midwife to oceanography. *Sea Frontiers,* **18** (5): 291-305.

RICE, A.L. 1975. The oceanography of John Ross's Arctic Expedition of 1818; a re-appraisal. *Journal of the Society for the Bibliography of Natural History,* **7**: 291-319.

RICE, A.L. 1983. Thomas Henry Huxley and the strange case of *Bathybius haeckelii;* a possible alternative explanation. *Archives of Natural History,* **II** (2): 169-180.

RICE, A.L 1986. *Deep-Sea Challenge: The John Murray/Mabahiss Expedition (1933-34); a 50th Anniversary Volume.* Paris: Unesco.

RICE, A.L., BURSTYN, H.L. and JONES, A.G.E. 1976. G.C. Wallich M.D.–megalomaniac or mis-used oceanographic genius? *Journal of the Society for the Bibliography of Natural History,* **7**: 423-450.

RICHARDSON, J. 1844-1848. *Zoology of the voyage of H.M.S. Erebus and Terror, under the command of Captain Sir James Clark Ross, during 1839-43. Ichthyology.* London: Vol. 2, pt. 2, 139pp. + 60 plates.

RICHARDSON, J. and GRAY, J.E. [Eds] 1844-1875. *The Zoology of H.M.S. Erebus and Terror, under the command of Captain Sir James Clark Ross, R.N., F.R.S., during the years 1839 to 1843.* London: Longman, Brown, Green and Longmans, 2 vols.

RITCHIE, G.S. 1957. *Challenger. The Life of a Survey Ship.* London: Hollis and Carter, XII + 249pp.

RITCHIE, G.S. 1967. *The Admiralty Chart. British naval hydrography in the nineteenth century.* London: Hollis and Carter, XII + 388pp.

ROSS, J. 1819. *A voyage of discovery, made under the orders of the Admiralty, in His Majesty's Ships Isabella and Alexander, for the purpose of exploring Baffin's Bay, and inquiring into the probability of a North West Passage.* London: John Murray, XXXIX + 252pp. + cxliv.

ROSS, J. 1835. *Narrative of a second voyage in search of a North-West Passage, and of a residence in the Arctic Regions during the years 1829, 1830, 1831, 1832, 1833. . . with Appendix. Including the reports of Commander, now Captain, James Clark Ross, R.N. . . . and the discovery of the northern magnetic pole.* London: A.W. Webster, XXXIV + 740, XII + 120 + CXLIV + CIIIpp.

ROSS, J.C. 1847. *A voyage of discovery and research in the southern and Antarctic regions during the years 1839-1843.* London: John Murray, 2 vols., 366 + 447pp. [Reprinted 1969 by David and Charles].

ROSS, J.C. 1854. On the effect of the pressure of the atmosphere on the mean level of the ocean. *Philosophical Transactions of the Royal Society of London,* **144**: 285-296.

ROSS, M.J. 1982. *Ross in the Antarctic,* Whitby: Caedmon of Whitby Press, 276pp.

SABINE, E. 1823. On the temperature at considerable depths in the Caribbean Sea. *Philosophical Transactions of the Royal Society of London*, **113**: 206-210.

SAVOURS, A. and McCONNELL, A. 1982. The history of the Rossbank Observatory, Tasmania. *Annals of Science*, **39**: 527-564.

SCHLEE, S. 1975. *A history of oceanography: the edge of an unfamiliar world*. London: Robert Hale and Company, 398pp.

SCHUESSLER, R. 1896. The mystery of the *Erebus* and *Terror*. *Sea Frontiers*, **32**: 20-26.

SCORESBY, W. 1820. *An account of the Arctic Regions with a history and description of the northern whale fishery*. Edinburgh: Archibald, Robertson and Co. 2 vols., 551 and 558pp.

SCORESBY, W. 1823. *Journal of a voyage to the Northern Whale Fishery*. Edinburgh: Archibald Constable and Co., XIIIL + 472pp.

SCOTT, R.F. 1905. *The voyage of the "Discovery"*, London: Smith, Elder and Co., 2 vols., XX + 556, XII + 508pp.

SEEMAN, B. 1853. *Narrative of the voyage of H.M.S. Herald during the years 1845-51 under the command of Captain Henry Kellett, R.N., C.B., being a circumnavigation of the globe and three cruises to the Arctic regions in search of Sir John Franklin*. London: Reeve and Co., 2 vols., 322 + 302pp.

SEWELL, R.B.S. 1925. Geographical and oceanographical research in Indian waters, 2. A study of the nature of the sea-bed and of the deep-sea deposits of the Andaman Sea and Bay of Bengal. *Memoirs of the Asiatic Society of Bengal*, **9**: 27-50.

SEWELL, R.B.S. 1935. Geographical and oceanographical research in Indian waters, 7. The topography and bottom deposits of the Laccadive Sea. *Memoirs of the Asiatic Society of Bengal*, **9**: 425-440.

SEWELL, R.B.S. 1952. Deep-sea oceanographic exploration in Indian waters. *Journal of the Bombay Natural History Society*, **50** (4): 705-717.

SHACKLETON, E.H. 1909. *The heart of the Antarctic: being the story of the British Antarctic Expedition 1907-1909*. London: William Heinemann, 2 vols., 372 + 418pp.

SHACKLETON, E.H. 1919. *South: the story of Shackleton's last expedition 1914-1917*. London: William Heinemann, 376pp.

SHARPE, R. Bowdler and BELL, F. Jeffrey (Eds) 1902. *Report on the collections of natural history made in the antarctic regions during the voyage of the "Southern Cross"*. London: British Museum (Natural History), 344pp.

SHORTLAND, P.F. 1869. *Sounding voyage of Her Majesty's Ship "Hydra"*. London: Hydrographic Office, 48pp.

SMITH, E.A. 1906. Mollusca, pp. 701-730 in *The History of the Collections contained in the Natural History Department of the British Museum*. London: British Museum (Natural History), Vol. 2, 782pp.

SMITH, W.C. [Ed.] 1930. *Report on the geological collections made during the voyage of the "Quest" on the Shackleton-Rowett Expedition to the South Atlantic and Weddell Sea in 1921-1922*. London: British Museum (Natural History), 161pp.

SOMERVILLE, H.B.T. 1900. *Report on the sounding cruise of HMS "Egeria" (Commander Morris H. Smyth) on the proposed Pacific cable route*. London: H.M.S.O., 12pp.

SOMERVILLE, H.B.T. 1928. *The chart makers*. Edinburgh: Blackwood.

SPRATT, T.A.B. 1857. *Report of deep soundings between Malta and the Archipelago in 1856 and 1857,—with remarks on the best means of obtaining deep soundings*. London: Hydrographic Office, 23pp.

SPRATT, T.A.B. 1857. Report on deep soundings between Malta and the Archipelago in 1856 and 1857, with remarks on the best means of obtaining deep soundings. *Nautical Magazine*, **26**: 393-412.

SPRATT, T.A.B. 1865. *Travels and Researches in Crete*, London: van Voorst, 2 vols., XII + 387 + IX + 435pp.

SPRY, W.J.J. 1895. *The cruise of Her Majesty's Ship "Challenger". Voyages over many seas, scenes from many lands*. London: Sampson Low, Marston and Co., 12th Edn., 319pp.

STAMP, T. and STAMP, C. 1976. *William Scoresby, Arctic scientist*. Whitby: Caedmon of Whitby Press, 253pp.

STEARN, W.T. 1981. *The Natural History Museum at South Kensington*. London: Heinemann, XXIII + 414pp.

STODDART, D. 1972. Buchanan—the forgotten apostle. *Geographical Magazine*, **44**: 858-862.

SWIRE, H. 1938. *The voyage of the Challenger*. London: Golden Cockerel Press, 2 vols., 191 + 169pp.

TAYLOR, F.J.R. 1980. Phytoplankton ecology before 1900: supplementary notes to the "Depths of the Ocean". Pp. 509-521 in Sears, M. and Merriman, D. [Eds] *Oceanography: the past*. New York: Springer-Verlag, 812pp.

THOMPSON, R.D. 1958. *D'Arcy Wentworth Thompson: The Scholar Naturalist*. London: Oxford University Press, XI + 244pp.

THOMPSON, S.P. 1910. *Life of Sir William Thomson, Baron Kelvin of Largs*. London: Macmillan, 2 vols., 1297pp.

THOMSON, A.S. 1896. Remarks on ocean currents, and practical hints on the method of their observation. *Report of the Sixth International Geographical Congress* (1895), London, 443-459.

THOMSON, C.W. 1873. *The Depths of the Sea*, London: Macmillan and Co., 527pp.

THOMSON, C.W. 1877. *The voyage of the Challenger. The Atlantic. A preliminary account of the general results of the exploring voyage of H.M.S. Challenger during the year 1873 and the early part of the year 1876*. London: 2 vols., 434 + 396pp.

THOMSON, C.W. 1880. The cruise of the *Knight Errant. Nature, London*, **22**: 405-407.

THOMSON, W. 1873-1875. On deep-sea soundings by pianoforte wire. *Proceedings of the Philosophical Society of Glasgow*, **9**: 111-117.

TIZARD, T.H. 1894. *Deep sea exploration in Faeroe Channel, by H.M.S. Triton, 1882*. London: Hydrographic Department. [Publication H.D. 141].

TIZARD, T.H. 1883. Remarks on the soundings and temperatures obtained in the Faeroe Channel during the summer of 1882. *Proceedings of the Royal Society of London*, **35**: 206-226.

TIZARD, T.H. 1900. *Chronological list of the officers conducting British maritime discoveries and surveys together with the names of the vessels employed from the earliest times until 1900*. London: H.M.S.O., 41pp.

TIZARD, T.H. and MURRAY, J. 1882. Exploration of the Faeroe Channel, during summer of 1880, in H.M.'s hired ship *Knight Errant. Proceedings of the Royal Society of Edinburgh*, 11: 638-724.

TUCKEY, J.K. 1816. *Narrative of an expedition to explore the River Zaire, usually called the Congo in South Africa, in 1816*. London: John Murray, xxxii + 498pp.

TUTEIN, P., 1938. *The sealers*. London: Casell, 247pp.

WALKER, F.M. 1984. *Song of the Clyde. A history of Clyde shipbuilding*. Cambridge: Patrick Stephens.

WALLICH, G.C. 1862. *The North-Atlantic Sea-Bed: comprising a diary of the voyage on board H.M.S. Bulldog, in 1860; and observations on the presence of animal life, and the formation and nature of organic deposits, at great depths in the Ocean*. London: John van Voorst, 160pp.

WASHINGTON, J. 1842. Tide observations—North Sea—Professor Whewell's Theory. *Nautical Magazine*, (1842): 566-569.

WAUCHOPE, R. 1822. Meteorological and hydrographical notes. *Memoirs of the Wernerian Natural History Society, Edinburgh*, **IV** (1): 161-172.

WAUCHOPE, R. 1836-39. Quantity of saline matter in deep and surface sea-water obtained in lat. 0°33'N, and long. 8°16'E; also result of three experiments on the temperature of the sea at great depths; and state of the barometer and thermometer during gale of wind off the Cape of Good Hope. *Edinburgh New Philosophical Journal*, **26**: 399-401.

WEBSTER, W.H.B. 1834. *Narrative of a voyage to the South Atlantic Ocean in the years 1828, 29, 30 performed by H.M. Sloop Chanticleer*. London: 2 vols., 399 + 398pp.

WENT, A.E.J. 1972. The role of the Royal Dublin Society (established in 1731) in fisheries research and development. *Proceedings of the Royal Society of Edinburgh*, B, **73**: 345-350.

WENT, A.E.J. 1972. Four late nineteenth century expeditions organised by the Royal Irish Academy. *Proceedings of the Royal Society of Edinburgh*, B, **72**: 305-309.

WHARTON, W.J.L. 1896. The deepest sounding yet known. *Nature, London*, **39**: 424-428.

WHARTON, W.J.L. 1898. *Report on the undercurrents in the Straits of Bab-el-Mandeb*. London: Hydrographic Department.

WHARTON, W.J.L. 1898. Undercurrents in the Strait of Bab-el-Mandeb. *Nature, London*, **58**: 544.

WHITE, R.S. 1984. Active and passive plate boundaries around the Gulf of Oman, north-west Indian Ocean. *Deep-Sea Research*, **31**: 731-745.

WILD, F. 1923a. The voyage of the "Quest". *Geographical Journal* 1923: 33-108.

WILD, F. 1923b. *Shackleton's last voyage. The story of the "Quest".* London: Cassel, 372pp.

WILD, J.J. 1877. *Thalassa: an essay on the depth, temperature, and currents of the ocean.* London: Marcus Ward, 140pp.

WILD, J.J. 1878. *At anchor: a narrative of experiences afloat and ashore during the voyage of H.M.S. "Challenger" from 1872-76.* London and Belfast: Marcus Ward and Co., 198pp.

WILLEMÖES-SUHM, R. von 1877. *Challenger Briefe.* Leipzig: Wilhelm Engelman, 180pp.

WILLIAMS-ELLIS, A. 1966. *Darwin's Moon. A biography of Alfred Russel Wallace.* London and Glasgow: Blackie, 261pp.

WILSON, E. 1966. *Discovery diaries.* Blandford Press.

WILSON, J.B. 1979. Biogenic carbonate sediments on the British Continental Shelf and on Rockall Bank. *Marine Geology,* **33**: M85-M93.

WOLFENDEN, R.N. 1909. *Scientific and biological researches in the North Atlantic conducted by the author on his yachts 'The Walwin' and 'The Silver Belle'.* London: Rebman Ltd. 234pp. [Memoirs of the Challenger Society, No. 1].

WOLLASTON, W.H. 1829. On the water of the Mediterranean. *Philosophical Transactions of the Royal Society of London,* **119**: 29-31.

WORDIE, J.M. 1918. The drift of the *Endurance. Geographical Journal,* 1918: 216-237.

WORDIE, J.M. 1921. The Ross Sea drift of the "Aurora" in 1915-1916. *Geographical Journal,* **58**: 219-224.

WÜST, G. 1964. The major deep-sea expeditions and research vessels 1873-1960. *Progress in Oceanography,* **2**: 3-52.

YONGE, C.M. 1972a. The inception and significance of the *Challenger* Expedition. *Proceedings of the Royal Society of Edinburgh,* B, **72**: 1-13.

YONGE, C.M. 1972b. Dredging life from ocean depths. *Geographical Magazine,* **44**: 867-870.

YOUNG, A. 1879. *The two voyages of the "Pandora" in 1875 and 1876.* London: VIII + 197pp.

INDEX TO PERSONNEL

Abel, Clarke
Alceste

Agassiz, Alexander
Medusa
Oceana
Research (built 1888)

Ainsworth, G.F.
Aurora

Aird, D.
Castlereagh

Alcock, A.W.
Investigator (built 1881)

Aldrich, Pelham
Alert
Challenger (built 1858)
Egeria
Flying Fish
Research (built 1888)
Terra Nova

Allman, G.J.
Valorous

Amherst, Lord
Alceste

Amundsen, Roald
Aurora
Endurance
Nimrod
Southern Cross
Terra Nova

Anderson, A.R.S.
Investigator (built 1881)

Archer, Colin
Southern Cross

Armstrong, J.
Clyde

Ault, J.P.
Research (launched 1939)

Back, George
Terror

Baillie, C.W.
Challenger (built 1858)

Balfour, A.F.
Penguin

Balfour, Francis Maitland
Sealark

Banks, Joseph
Alceste
Esk
Investigator (purchased 1798)
Isabella (1818)

Barrow, John
Congo
Isabella (1818)

Bassett-Smith, P.W.
Egeria
Penguin

Baudin, Nicolas
Investigator (purchased 1798)

Bauer, Ferdinand
Investigator (purchased 1798)

Beamish, C.H.T.
Harlequin

Bedford, Edward J.
Lightning

Beechey, Frederick William
Blossom
Dorothea
Lightning
Sulphur

Belcher, Edward
Lightning
Samarang
Sulphur

Bell, F. Jeffrey
Discovery (built 1901)
Southern Cross

Bennett, James Gordon
Pandora (built 1861)

Bernacchi, Louis
Southern Cross

Berryman, Otway
Cyclops

Bethel, G.R.
Challenger (built 1858)
Shearwater (built 1861)

Bidder, G.P.
Huxley

Bill, R.
Challenger (built 1931)

Blackburn, J.
L6

Blackburn, J.F.
Discovery II

Blackman, Vernon Herbert
Oceana

Blackwood, Francis P.
Castlereagh
Fly

Croll, James
Porcupine

Crozier, Francis R.M.
Erebus
Terror

Cunningham, R.O.
Nassau

Daniel, E.T.
Beacon

Dannevig, H.C.
Aurora

Darwin, Charles
Beagle
Cyclops
Erebus

David, Peter M.
Discovery II

David, T.W. Edgeworth
Nimrod

Davidson, Robert
Diana

Davis, John King
Aurora
Discovery (built 1901)

Dayman, Joseph
Bulldog
Cyclops
Erebus
Firebrand
Gorgon
Porcupine
Rattlesnake

Daussy, Pierre
Enterprise

Deacon, George E.R.
Discovery II

De Long, Lieut. U.S.N.
Pandora (built 1861)

Denham, Henry
Herald

Derby, Earl of
Fly

Dickie, G.
Valorous

Dickson, Henry N.
Jackal
Silver Belle

Donald, C.W.
Active

Douglas, E.
Discovery (built 1901)

Douglas, H.P.
Goldfinch

Drygalski, E. von
Scotia

Duncan, P.M.
Valorous

Edmondson, T.
Herald

Ehrenberg, Christian
Erebus

Ellsworth, Lincoln
Discovery II

Elson, Thomas,
Blossom

England, Rupert G.
Nimrod

Evans, E.R.G.
Terra Nova

Evans, F.J.O.
Knight Errant

Evans, F.P.
Nimrod

Evans, Hugh Blackwall
Southern Cross

Ewing, Maurice
Challenger (built 1931)

Fairweather, Alexander
Balaena

Falla, R.A.
Discovery (built 1901)

Faouzi, H.
Mabahiss

Farquhar, Arthur M.
Jackal

Farquharson, W.I.
Mabahiss

Farran, G.P.
Silver Belle

Field, A.M.
Egeria
Penguin
Research (built 1888)

Fisher, George
Hecla

Fitzroy, Robert
Adventure (built 1809)
Adventure (purchased 1833)
Beagle
Erebus

Fletcher, H.O.
Discovery (built 1901)

Fletcher, Lazarus
Oceana

Flinders, Matthew
Investigator (purchased 1798)

Flynn, T.
Aurora

Mill, Hugh Robert
Aurora
Jackal
Medusa
Newport
Miller, William Allen
Porcupine
Mills, Sir James
Nimrod
Mohamed, Abdel Fatteh
Mabahiss
Moore, Thomas Edward Laws
Pagoda
Moore, W. Usborne
Penguin
Research (built 1888)
Moseley, Henry Nottidge
Challenger (built 1858)
Moyes, M.H.
Discovery (built 1901)
Moyne, Lord (see also Guinness, B.W.)
Rosaura
Murchison, Roderick
Bulldog
Murray, George
Oceana
Murray, James
Nimrod
Murray, John
Britannia
Challenger (built 1858)
Cyclops
Egeria
Flying Fish
Gannet
Investigator (built 1907)
Jackal
Knight Errant
Lalla Rookh
Mabahiss
Medusa
Oceana
Triton
Murray, John Challenger
Mabahiss
Mutsuhito, Emperor of Japan
Challenger (built 1858)
Nansen, Fridtjof
Pandora (built 1861)
Nares, George Strong
Alert
Challenger (built 1858)
Discovery (purchased 1874)
Flying Fish
Newport
Pandora (built 1861)
Salamander
Shearwater (built 1861)
Valorous

Nelson, A.L.
Discovery II
Nelson, E.W.
Terra Nova
Newnes, Sir George
Southern Cross
Ninnis, B.E.S.
Aurora
Nordenskjöld, Otto
Scotia
Norman, A.M.
Valorous
Norman, J.R.
Discovery (built 1901)
Oldham, Cecil F.
Lark
Ommanney, F.D.
Discovery II
Otter, H.C.
Porcupine
Parker, I.P.
Herald
Parr, A.C.C.
Alert
Parry, William Edward
Alexander
Fury
Griper
Hecla
Isabella (1818)
Pheasant
Peake, R.F.
Britannia
Pearcy, Frank
Knight Errant
Pennell, H.L.L.
Terra Nova
Percival, George
Knight Errant
Péron, François
Investigator (purchased 1798)
Pettersson, Otto
Jackal
Phipps, Constantine John
Fury
Isabella (1818)
Pirie, George
Pandora (built 1861)
Poole, T.H.
Fingal
Popham, F. Leybourne
Newport
Price, Grenfell
Discovery (built 1901)
Priestley, Raymond
Nimrod

GENERAL INDEX

Tartarus, H.M.S.
  Medina

Tasmania
  Discovery (built 1901)

Telegraph Construction and Maintenance Company
  Alert
  Britannia
  Dacia

Termagant
  Herald

Terra Nova
  Aurora
  Discovery (built 1901)

Terror, H.M.S.
  Alert
  Bulldog
  Fury
  Herald
  Lightning
  Pagoda
  Pandora (built 1861)
  Scotia

Thermometers
  Johnson's metallic
    Porcupine

  Miller-Casella
    Challenger (built 1858)
    Porcupine
    Walwin

  Negretti and Zambra
    Challenger (built 1858)
    Sealark
    Southern Cross
    Walwin

  Richter's reversing
    Aurora
    Sealark
    Terra Nova

  Siemen's electrical
    Challenger (built 1858)

  Six
    Blossom
    Challenger (built 1858)
    Chanticleer
    Erebus
    Esk
    Hecla
    Isabella (1818)
    Rattlesnake

Tahiti
  Alert
  Challenger (built 1858)

Three King's Islands
  Terra Nova

Thunder
  Fury

Tidal observations
  Discovery (built 1901)
  Fairy
  Shearwater

Timor
  Investigator (purchased 1798)

Titanic, S.S.
  Scotia

Toroa, S.S.
  Aurora

Tow-nets
  Challenger (built 1858)
  Discovery (built 1901)
  Research (built 1888)
  Rosaura
  Sealark
  Silver Belle

Transatlantic telegraph cable
  Bulldog
  Cyclops

Transit of Venus
  Shearwater (built 1861)

Transparency
  Rosaura

Trawl
  Agassiz (= Monegasque)
    Aurora
    Challenger (built 1858)
    Flying Falcon
    Investigator (built 1881)
    Rosaura
    Sealark
    Silver Belle

  Beam
    Challenger (built 1858)
    Fingal
    Garland
    Harlequin
    Silver Belle

Treasury (U.K.)
  Challenger (built 1858)

Trent, H.M.S.
  Congo
  Dorothea
  Isabella (1818)

Tridacna (mollusc)
  Fly

Trieste
  Challenger (built 1931)

Tristan da Cunha
  Challenger (built 1858)
  Discovery (built 1901)